INTEGRATE

THE PEARSON CUSTOM LIBRARY FOR

anatomy & physiology

Cat Dissection Guide
Human Biology 101
Georgetown University

PEARSON

...atomy & Physiology Team

...Chief: Serina Beauparlant
...e Editor: Leslie Berriman
Acq...ons Editor: Gretchen Puttkamer
Sr. Project Editor: Robin Pille
Associate Editor: Shannon Cutt
Associate Editor: Katie Seibel
Art Development Manager: Laura Southworth
Development Editor: Alice Fugate
Editorial Assistant: Lisa Damerel
Sr. Managing Editor: Deborah Cogan
Executive Media Producer: Liz Winer
Marketing Manager: Derek Perrigo

Pearson Learning Solutions

Senior Vice President, Editorial: Patrick F. Boles
Senior Sponsoring Editor: Natalie Danner
Development Editor: Jill Johnson
Executive Marketing Manager: Nathan L. Wilbur
Operations Manager: Eric M. Kenney
Production Manager: Jennifer Berry
Art Director: Renée Sartell
Cover Designer: Kristen Kiley

Cover Art: Courtesy of DK Images and Prentice-Hall, Inc. "Swim Start 30," courtesy of iStockphoto. "Male Gymnast Performing on the Pommel Horse," courtesy of Veer Images.

This special edition published in cooperation with Pearson Learning Solutions.

Printed in the United States of America.
7 16
Please visit our website at *www.pearsonlearningsolutions.com*.

Attention bookstores: For permission to return unused stock, contact us at *pe-uscustomreturns@pearson.com*.

Pearson Learning Solutions, 501 Boylston Street, Suite 900, Boston, MA 02116
A Pearson Education Company
www.pearsoned.com

ISBN 10: 1-256-24636-0
ISBN 13: 978-1-256-24636-7

Laboratory Safety: General Guidelines

1. Notify your instructor immediately if you are pregnant, color blind, allergic to any insects or chemicals, taking immunosuppressive drugs, or have any other medical condition (such as diabetes, immunologic defect) that may require special precautionary measures in the laboratory.

2. Upon entering the laboratory, place all books, coats, purses, backpacks, etc. in designated areas, not on the bench tops.

3. Locate and, when appropriate, learn to use exits, fire extinguisher, fire blanket, chemical shower, eyewash, first aid kit, broken glass container, and cleanup materials for spills.

4. In case of fire, evacuate the room and assemble outside the building.

5. Do not eat, drink, smoke, or apply cosmetics in the laboratory.

6. Confine long hair, loose clothing, and dangling jewelry.

7. Wear shoes at all times in the laboratory.

8. Cover any cuts or scrapes with a sterile, waterproof bandage before attending lab.

9. Wear eye protection when working with chemicals.

10. Never pipet by mouth. Use mechanical pipeting devices.

11. Wash skin immediately and thoroughly if contaminated by chemicals or microorganisms.

12. Do not perform unauthorized experiments.

13. Do not use equipment without instruction.

14. Report all spills and accidents to your instructor immediately.

15. Never leave heat sources unattended.

16. When using hot plates, note that there is no visible sign that they are hot (such as a red glow). Always assume that hot plates are hot.

17. Use an appropriate apparatus when handling hot glassware.

18. Keep chemicals away from direct heat or sunlight.

19. Keep containers of alcohol, acetone, and other flammable liquids away from flames.

20. Do not allow any liquid to come into contact with electrical cords. Handle electrical connectors with dry hands. Do not attempt to disconnect electrical equipment that crackles, snaps, or smokes.

21. Upon completion of laboratory exercises, place all materials in the disposal areas designated by your instructor.

22. Do not pick up broken glassware with your hands. Use a broom and dustpan and discard the glass in designated glass waste containers; never discard with paper waste.

23. Wear disposable gloves when working with blood, other body fluids, or mucous membranes. Change gloves after possible contamination and wash hands immediately after gloves are removed.

24. The disposal symbol indicates that items that may have come in contact with body fluids should be placed in your lab's designated container. It also refers to liquid wastes that should not be poured down the drain into the sewage system.

25. Leave the laboratory clean and organized for the next student.

26. Wash your hands with liquid or powdered soap prior to leaving the laboratory.

27. The biohazard symbol indicates procedures that may pose health concerns.

The caution symbol points out instruments, substances, and procedures that require special attention to safety. These symbols appear throughout this manual.

Measurement Conversions

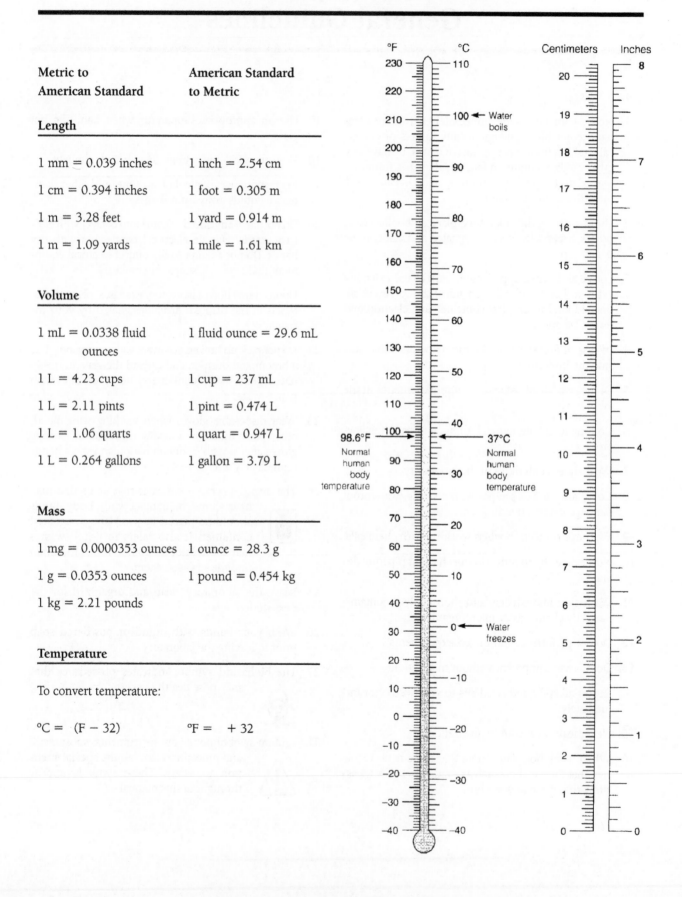

Metric to American Standard

American Standard to Metric

Length

Metric to American Standard	American Standard to Metric
1 mm = 0.039 inches	1 inch = 2.54 cm
1 cm = 0.394 inches	1 foot = 0.305 m
1 m = 3.28 feet	1 yard = 0.914 m
1 m = 1.09 yards	1 mile = 1.61 km

Volume

Metric to American Standard	American Standard to Metric
1 mL = 0.0338 fluid ounces	1 fluid ounce = 29.6 mL
1 L = 4.23 cups	1 cup = 237 mL
1 L = 2.11 pints	1 pint = 0.474 L
1 L = 1.06 quarts	1 quart = 0.947 L
1 L = 0.264 gallons	1 gallon = 3.79 L

Mass

Metric to American Standard	American Standard to Metric
1 mg = 0.0000353 ounces	1 ounce = 28.3 g
1 g = 0.0353 ounces	1 pound = 0.454 kg
1 kg = 2.21 pounds	

Temperature

To convert temperature:

$$°C = \ (F - 32)$$

$$°F = \quad + 32$$

98.6°F — Normal human body temperature

37°C — Normal human body temperature

100 ← Water boils

0 ← Water freezes

Contents

Dissection and Identification of Cat Muscles

MATERIALS

☐ Disposable gloves or protective skin cream
☐ Preserved and injected cat (one for every two to four students)
☐ Dissecting instruments and tray
☐ Name tag and large plastic bag
☐ Paper towels
☐ Embalming fluid
☐ Organic debris container

OBJECTIVES

1. To name and locate muscles on a dissected cat.
2. To recognize similarities and differences between human and cat musculature.

The skeletal muscles of all mammals are named in a similar fashion. However, some muscles that are separate in lower animals are fused in humans, and some muscles present in lower animals are lacking in humans. This exercise involves dissection of the cat musculature to enhance your knowledge of the human muscular system. Since the aim is to become familiar with the muscles of the human body, you should pay particular attention to the similarities between cat and human muscles. However, pertinent differences will be pointed out as you encounter them.

Wear a lab coat or apron over your clothes when dissecting to prevent staining your clothes with embalming fluid. Also, read through this entire exercise before coming to the lab.

ACTIVITY 1

Preparing the Cat for Dissection

The preserved laboratory animals purchased for dissection have been embalmed with a solution that prevents deterioration of the tissues. The animals are generally delivered in plastic bags that contain a small amount of the embalming fluid. _Do not dispose of this fluid_ when you remove the cat; the fluid prevents the cat from drying out. It is very important to keep the cat's tissues moist because you will probably use the same cat from now until the end of the course. The embalming fluid may cause your eyes to smart and may dry your skin, but these small irritants are preferable to working with a cat that has become hard and odoriferous because of bacterial action.

1. Don disposable gloves and then obtain a cat, dissecting tray, dissecting instruments, and a name tag. Using a pencil, mark the name tag with the names of the members of your group and set it aside. The name tag will be attached to the plastic bag at the end of the dissection so that you may identify your animal in subsequent laboratory sessions.

2. To begin removing the skin, place the cat ventral side down on the dissecting tray. Cutting away from yourself with a newly bladed scalpel, make a short, shallow incision in the midline of the neck, just to penetrate the skin. From this point on, use scissors. Continue to cut the length of the back to the sacrolumbar region, stopping at the tail (Figure 1).

3. From the dorsal surface of the tail region, continue the incision around the tail, encircling the anus and genital organs. The skin will not be removed from this region.

4. Beginning again at the dorsal tail region, make an incision through the skin down each hind leg nearly to the ankle.* Continue the cuts completely around the ankles.

5. Return to the neck. Cut the skin around the circumference of the neck.

PAL
For access to anatomical models and more, check out Practice Anatomy Lab.

From Dissection Exercise 1 of _Human Anatomy & Physiology Laboratory Manual, PhysioEx 9.0 Update, Cat Version_, Tenth Edition.
Elaine N. Marieb, Susan J. Mitchell. Copyright © 2012 by Pearson Education, Inc. Published by Pearson Benjamin Cummings. All rights reserved.

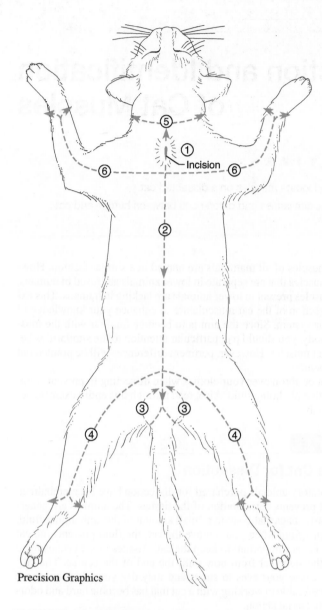

Incision

FIGURE 1 Incisions to be made in skinning a cat. Numbers indicate sequence.

6. Cut down each foreleg to the wrist.* Completely cut through the skin around the wrists (see Figure 1).

7. Now free the skin from the loose connective tissue (superficial fascia) that binds it to the underlying structures. With one hand, grasp the skin on one side of the midline dorsal incision. Then, using your fingers or a blunt probe, break through the "cottony" connective tissue fibers to release the skin from the muscle beneath. Work toward the ventral surface and then toward the neck. As you pull the skin from the body, you should see small, white, cordlike structures extending from the skin to the muscles at fairly regular intervals. These are the cutaneous nerves that serve the skin. You will also see (particularly as you approach the ventral surface) that a thin layer of muscle fibers remains adhered to the skin. This is the **cutaneous maximus** muscle, which enables the cat to

*Check with your instructor. He or she may want you to skin only the right or left side of the cat.

move its skin rather like our facial muscles allow us to express emotion. Where the cutaneous maximus fibers cling to those of the deeper muscles, they should be carefully cut free. Along the ventral surface of the trunk, notice the two lines of nipples associated with the mammary glands. These are more prominent in females, especially if they are pregnant or were recently lactating.

8. You will notice as you start to free the skin in the neck that it is more difficult to remove. Take extra care and time in this area. The large flat **platysma** muscle in the ventral neck region (a skin muscle like the cutaneous maximus) will remain attached to the skin. The skin will not be removed from the head since the cat's muscles are not sufficiently similar to human head muscles to merit study.

9. Complete the skinning process by freeing the skin from the forelimbs, the lower torso, and the hindlimbs in the same manner. The skin may be more difficult to remove as you approach the paws so you may need to take additional time in these areas to avoid damaging the underlying muscles and tendons. *Do not discard the skin.*

10. Inspect your skinned cat. Notice that it is difficult to see any cleavage lines between the muscles because of the overlying connective tissue, which is white or yellow. If time allows, carefully remove as much of the fat and fascia from the surface of the muscles as possible, using forceps or your fingers. The muscles, when exposed, look grainy or threadlike and are light brown. If this clearing process is done carefully and thoroughly, you will be ready to begin your identification of the superficial muscles.

11. If the muscle dissection exercises are to be done at a later laboratory session, follow the cleanup instructions noted in the box below. *Prepare your cat for storage in this way every time the cat is used.* ■

Preparing the Dissection Animal for Storage

Before leaving the lab, prepare your animal for storage:

1. To prevent the internal organs from drying out, dampen a layer of folded paper towels with embalming fluid, and wrap them snugly around the animal's torso. (Do not use *water-soaked* paper towels, which encourages mold growth.) Make sure the dissected areas are completely enveloped.

2. Return the animal's skin flaps to their normal position over the ventral cavity body organs.

3. Place the animal in a plastic storage bag. Add more embalming fluid if necessary, press out excess air, and securely close the bag with a rubber band or twine.

4. Make sure your name tag is securely attached, and place the animal in the designated storage container.

5. Clean all dissecting equipment with soapy water, rinse, and dry it for return to the storage area. Wash down the lab bench and properly dispose of organic debris and your gloves before leaving the laboratory.

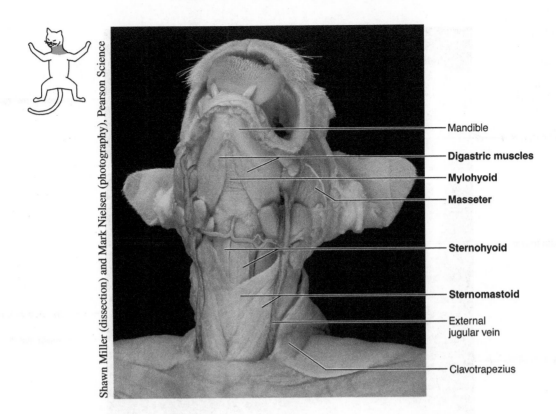

Shawn Miller (dissection) and Mark Nielsen (photography), Pearson Science

- Mandible
- **Digastric muscles**
- **Mylohyoid**
- **Masseter**
- **Sternohyoid**
- **Sternomastoid**
- External jugular vein
- Clavotrapezius

FIGURE 2 Superficial muscles of the anterior neck of the cat.

Dissecting Neck and Trunk Muscles

The proper dissection of muscles involves careful separation of one muscle from another and transection of superficial muscles in order to study those lying deeper. In general, when directions are given to transect a muscle, it first should be completely freed from all adhering connective tissue and *then* cut through the belly (fleshiest part) of the muscle about halfway between its origin and insertion points. *Use caution when working around points of muscle origin or insertion, and do not remove the fascia associated with such attachments.*

As a rule, all the fibers of one muscle are held together by a connective tissue sheath (epimysium) and run in the same general direction. Before you begin dissection, observe your skinned cat. If you look carefully, you can see changes in the direction of the muscle fibers, which will help you to locate the muscle borders. Pulling in slightly different directions on two adjacent muscles will usually expose subtle white lines created by the connective tissue surrounding the muscles and allow you to find the normal cleavage line between them. After you have identified cleavage lines, *use a blunt probe* to break the connective tissue between muscles and to separate them. If the muscles separate as clean, distinct bundles, your procedure is probably correct. If they appear ragged or chewed up, you are probably tearing a muscle apart rather than separating it from adjacent muscles. Only the muscles that are most easily identified and separated out will be identified in this exercise because of time considerations.

Anterior Neck Muscles

1. Using Figure 2 as a guide, examine the anterior neck surface of the cat and identify the following superficial neck muscles. (The *platysma* belongs in this group but was probably removed during the skinning process.) The **sternomastoid** muscle and the more lateral and deeper **cleidomastoid** muscle (not visible in Figure 2) are joined in humans to form the sternocleidomastoid. The large external jugular veins, which drain the head, should be obvious crossing the anterior aspect of these muscles. The **mylohyoid** muscle parallels the bottom aspect of the chin, and the **digastric** muscles form a V over the mylohyoid muscle. Although it is not one of the neck muscles, you can now identify the fleshy **masseter** muscle, which flanks the digastric muscle laterally. Finally, the **sternohyoid** is a narrow muscle between the mylohyoid (superiorly) and the inferior sternomastoid.

2. The deeper muscles of the anterior neck of the cat are small and straplike and hardly worth the effort of dissection. However, one of these deeper muscles can be seen with a minimum of extra effort. Transect the sternomastoid and sternohyoid muscles approximately at midbelly. Reflect the cut ends to reveal the bandlike **sternothyroid** muscle (not visible in Figure 2), which runs along the anterior surface of the throat just deep and lateral to the sternohyoid muscle. The cleidomastoid muscle, which lies deep to the sternomastoid, is also more easily identified now.

Superficial Chest Muscles

In the cat, the chest or pectoral muscles adduct the arm, just as they do in humans. However, humans have only two pectoral muscles, and cats have four—the pectoralis major, pectoralis

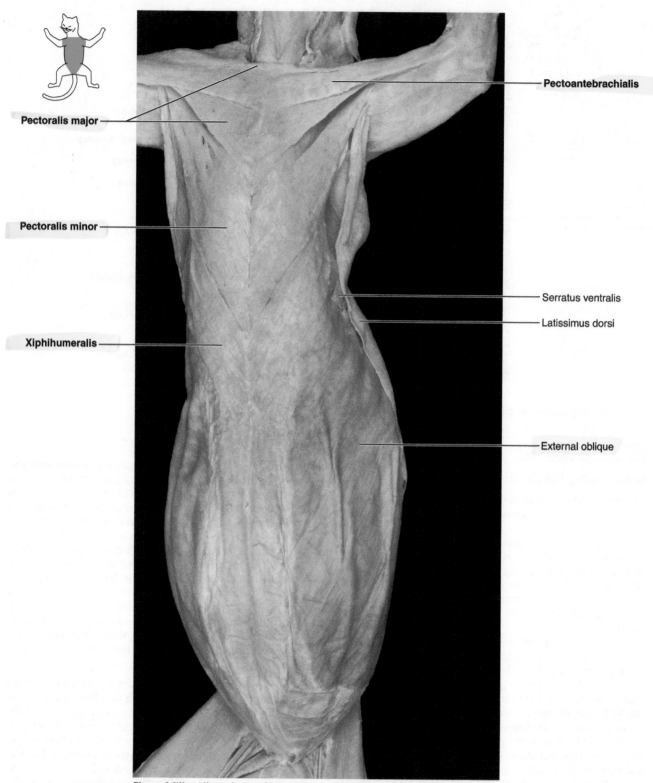

Pectoralis major

Pectoralis minor

Xiphihumeralis

Pectoantebrachialis

Serratus ventralis

Latissimus dorsi

External oblique

Shawn Miller (dissection) and Mark Nielsen (photography), Pearson Science

FIGURE 3 Superficial muscles of the thorax and abdominal wall, ventral view.
Note location of the latissimus dorsi.

minor, xiphihumeralis, and pectoantebrachialis (Figure 3). However, because of their relatively great degree of fusion, the cat's pectoral muscles appear to be a single muscle. The pectoral muscles are rather difficult to dissect and identify, as they do not separate from one another easily.

The **pectoralis major** is 5 to 8 cm (2 to 3 inches) wide and can be seen arising on the manubrium, just inferior to the sternomastoid muscle of the neck, and running to the humerus. Its fibers run at right angles to the longitudinal axis of the cat's body.

The **pectoralis minor** lies beneath the pectoralis major and extends posterior to it on the abdominal surface. It originates on the sternum and inserts on the humerus. Its fibers run obliquely to the long axis of the body, which helps to distinguish it from the pectoralis major. Contrary to what its name implies, the pectoralis minor is a larger and thicker muscle than the pectoralis major.

The **xiphihumeralis** can be distinguished from the posterior edge of the pectoralis minor only by virtue of the fact that its origin is lower—on the xiphoid process of the sternum. Its fibers run parallel to and are fused with those of the pectoralis minor.

The **pectoantebrachialis** is a thin, straplike muscle, about 1.3 cm (½ inch) wide, lying over the pectoralis major. Notice that the pectoralis major is visible both anterior and posterior to the borders of the pectoantebrachialis. It originates from the manubrium, passes laterally over the pectoralis major, and merges with the muscles of the forelimb approximately halfway down the humerus. It has no homologue in humans.

Identify, free, and trace out the origin and insertion of the cat's chest muscles. Refer to Figure 3 as you work.

Muscles of the Abdominal Wall

The superficial trunk muscles include those of the abdominal wall (Figures 3 and 4). Cat musculature in this area is quite similar in function to that of humans.

1. Complete the dissection of the more superficial anterior trunk muscles of the cat by identifying the origins and insertions of the muscles of the abdominal wall. Work carefully here. These muscles are very thin, and it is easy to miss their boundaries. Begin with the **rectus abdominis,** a long band of muscle approximately 2.5 cm (1 inch) wide running immediately lateral to the midline of the body on the abdominal surface. Humans have four transverse *tendinous intersections* in the rectus abdominis, but they are absent or difficult to identify in the cat. Identify the **linea alba,** the longitudinal band of connective tissue that separates the rectus abdominis muscles. Note the relationship of the rectus abdominis to the other abdominal muscles and their fascia.

2. The **external oblique** is a sheet of muscle immediately beside the rectus abdominis (see Figure 4). Carefully free and then transect the external oblique to reveal the anterior attachment of the rectus abdominis and the deeper **internal oblique.** Reflect the external oblique; observe the deeper muscle. Notice which way the fibers run.

How does the fiber direction of the internal oblique compare to that of the external oblique?

_____

_____

3. Free and then transect the internal oblique muscle to reveal the fibers of the **transversus abdominis,** whose fibers run transversely across the abdomen.

Superficial Muscles of the Shoulder and the Dorsal Trunk and Neck

Refer to Figure 5 as you dissect the superficial muscles of the dorsal surface of the trunk.

1. Turn your cat on its ventral surface, and start your observations with the **trapezius group.** Humans have a single large *trapezius muscle,* but the cat has three separate muscles—the clavotrapezius, acromiotrapezius, and spinotrapezius—that together perform a similar function. The prefix in each case (clavo-, acromio-, and spino-) reveals the muscle's site of insertion. The **clavotrapezius,** the most anterior muscle of the group, is homologous to that part of the human trapezius that inserts into the clavicle. Slip a probe under this muscle and follow it to its apparent origin.

Where does the clavotrapezius appear to originate?

_____

Is this similar to its origin in humans? _____

The fibers of the clavotrapezius are continuous posteriorly with those of the clavicular part of the cat's deltoid muscle (clavodeltoid), and the two muscles work together to flex the humerus. Release the clavotrapezius muscle from adjoining muscles. The **acromiotrapezius** is a large, thin, nearly square muscle easily identified by its aponeurosis, which passes over the vertebral border of the scapula. It originates from the cervical and T$_1$ vertebrae and inserts into the scapular spine. The triangular **spinotrapezius** runs from the thoracic vertebrae to the scapular spine. This is the most posterior of the trapezius muscles in the cat. Now that you know where they are located, pull on the three trapezius muscles to mimic their action.

Do the trapezius muscles appear to have the same functions in cats as in humans?

_____

2. The **levator scapulae ventralis,** a flat, straplike muscle, can be located in the triangle created by the division of the fibers of the clavotrapezius and acromiotrapezius. Its anterior fibers run underneath the clavotrapezius from its origin at the base of the skull (occipital bone), and it inserts on the vertebral border of the scapula. In the cat it helps to hold the upper edges of the scapulae together and draws them toward the head.

What is the function of the levator scapulae in humans?

_____

_____

5

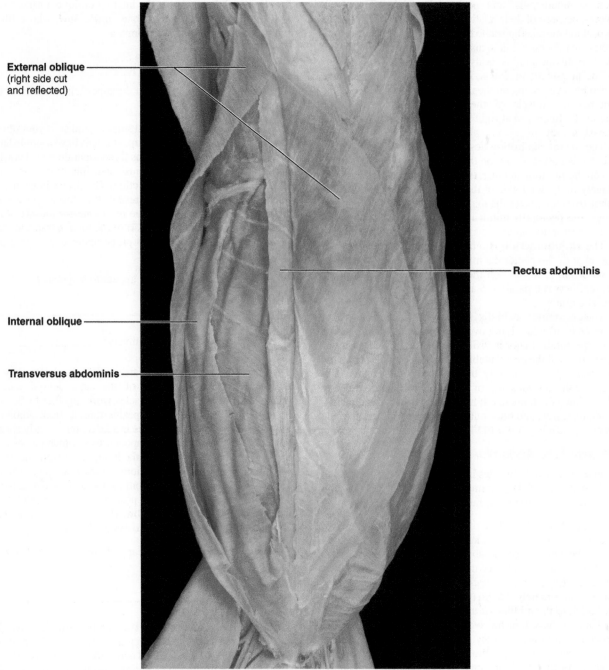

External oblique
(right side cut
and reflected)

Rectus abdominis

Internal oblique

Transversus abdominis

Shawn Miller (dissection) and Mark Nielsen (photography), Pearson Science

FIGURE 4 **Muscles of the abdominal wall of the cat.**

3.　The **deltoid group:** Like the trapezius, the human *deltoid muscle* is represented by three separate muscles in the cat—the clavodeltoid, acromiodeltoid, and spinodeltoid. The **clavodeltoid** (also called the *clavobrachialis*), the most superficial muscle of the shoulder, is a continuation of the clavotrapezius below the clavicle, which is this muscle's point of origin (see Figure 5). Follow its course down the forelimb to the point where it merges along a white line with the pectoantebrachialis. Separate it from the pectoantebrachialis, and then transect it and pull it back.

Where does the clavodeltoid insert? _____

What do you think the function of this muscle is?

_____

_____

　　The **acromiodeltoid** lies posterior to the clavodeltoid and runs over the top of the shoulder. This small triangular muscle originates on the acromion of the scapula. It inserts

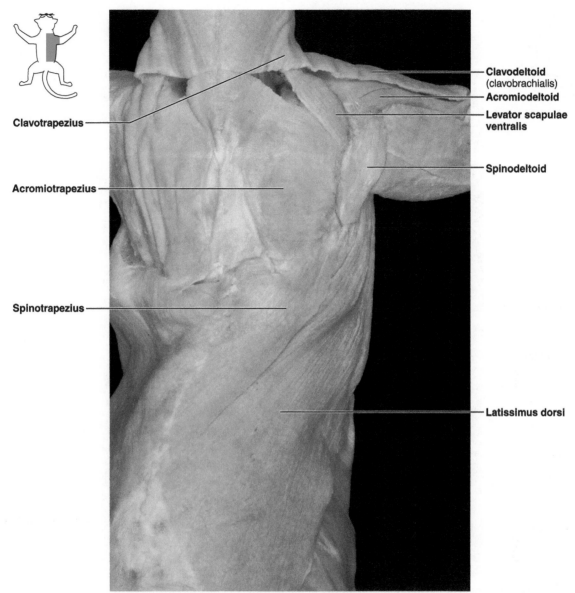

Clavotrapezius

Acromiotrapezius

Spinotrapezius

Clavodeltoid
(clavobrachialis)

Acromiodeltoid

Levator scapulae
ventralis

Spinodeltoid

Latissimus dorsi

Shawn Miller (dissection) and Mark Nielsen (photography), Pearson Science

FIGURE 5 Superficial muscles of the anterodorsal aspect of the shoulder, trunk, and neck of the cat.

into the spinodeltoid (a muscle of similar size) posterior to it. The **spinodeltoid** is covered with fascia near the anterior end of the scapula. Its tendon extends under the acromiodeltoid muscle and inserts on the humerus. Notice that its fibers run obliquely to those of the acromiodeltoid. Like the human deltoid muscle, the acromiodeltoid and spinodeltoid muscles in the cat abduct and rotate the humerus.

4. The **latissimus dorsi** is a large, thick, flat muscle covering most of the lateral surface of the posterior trunk; it extends and adducts the arm. Its anterior edge is covered by the spinotrapezius and may appear ragged because it has been cut off from the cutaneous maximus muscle attached to the skin. As in humans, it inserts into the humerus. But before inserting, its fibers merge with the fibers of many other muscles, among them the xiphihumeralis of the pectoralis group.

Deep Muscles of the Laterodorsal Trunk and Neck

1. In preparation for identifying deep muscles of the dorsal trunk, transect the latissimus dorsi, the muscles of the pectoralis group, and the spinotrapezius and reflect them back. Be careful not to damage the large brachial nerve plexus, which lies in the axillary space beneath the pectoralis group.

2. The **serratus ventralis** corresponds to two separate muscles in humans. The posterior portion is homologous to the *serratus anterior* of humans, arising deep to the pectoral muscles and covering the lateral surface of the rib cage. It is easily identified by its fingerlike muscular origins, which arise on the first 9 or 10 ribs. It inserts into the scapula. The anterior portion of the serratus ventralis, which arises from the cervical vertebrae, is homologous to the *levator scapulae* in humans; both pull the scapula toward the sternum. Trace this

7

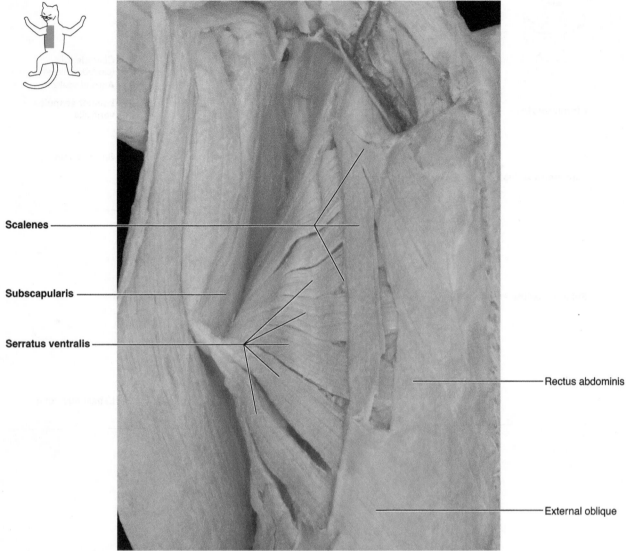

Shawn Miller (dissection) and Mark Nielsen (photography), Pearson Science

FIGURE 6 Deep muscles of the inferolateral thorax of the cat.

muscle to its insertion. In general, in the cat, this muscle pulls the scapula posteriorly and downward (Figure 6).

3.   Reflect the upper limb to reveal the **subscapularis**, which occupies most of the ventral surface of the scapula. Humans have a homologous muscle.

4.   Locate the anterior, posterior, and middle **scalene** muscles on the lateral surface of the cat's neck and trunk. The most prominent and longest of these muscles is the middle scalene, which lies between the anterior and posterior members. The scalenes originate on the ribs and run cephalad over the serratus ventralis to insert in common on the cervical vertebrae. These muscles draw the ribs anteriorly and bend the neck downward; thus they are homologous to the human scalene muscles, which elevate the ribs and flex the neck. (Notice that the difference is only one of position. Humans walk erect, but cats are quadrupeds.)

5.   Reflect the flaps of the transected latissimus dorsi, spinodeltoid, acromiodeltoid, and levator scapulae ventralis. The

splenius is a large flat muscle occupying most of the side of the neck close to the vertebrae (Figure 7). As in humans, it originates on the ligamentum nuchae at the back of the neck and inserts into the occipital bone. It raises the head.

6.   To view the rhomboid muscles, lay the cat on its side and hold its forelegs together to spread the scapulae apart. The rhomboid muscles lie between the scapulae and beneath the acromiotrapezius. All the rhomboid muscles originate on the vertebrae and insert on the scapula. They hold the dorsal part of the scapula to the cat's back.

   There are three rhomboids in the cat. The ribbonlike **rhomboid capitis,** the most anterolateral muscle of the group, has no counterpart in the human body. The **rhomboid minor,** located posterior to the rhomboid capitis, is much larger. The fibers of the rhomboid minor run transversely to those of the rhomboid capitis. The most posterior muscle of the group, the **rhomboid major,** is so closely fused to the rhomboid minor that many consider them to be one muscle—the **rhomboideus,** which is homologous to human *rhomboid muscles.*

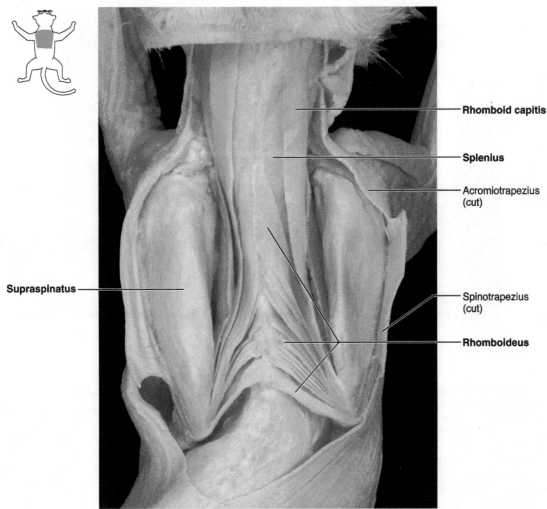

Shawn Miller (dissection) and Mark Nielsen (photography), Pearson Science

FIGURE 7 Deep muscles of the superior aspect of the dorsal thorax of the cat.

7. The **supraspinatus** and **infraspinatus** muscles are similar to the same muscles in humans. The supraspinatus can be found under the acromiotrapezius, and the infraspinatus is deep to the spinotrapezius. Both originate on the lateral scapular surface and insert on the humerus. ▬

ACTIVITY 3

Dissecting Forelimb Muscles

Cat forelimb muscles fall into the same three categories as human upper limb muscles, but in this section the muscles of the entire forelimb are considered together. Refer to Figure 8 as you study these muscles.

Muscles of the Lateral Surface

1. The triceps muscle **(triceps brachii)** of the cat is easily identified if the cat is placed on its side. It is a large fleshy muscle covering the posterior aspect and much of the side of the humerus. As in humans, this muscle arises from three heads, which originate from the humerus and scapula and insert jointly into the olecranon process of the ulna. Remove the

fascia from the superior region of the lateral arm surface to identify the lateral and long heads of the triceps. The long head is approximately twice as long as the lateral head and lies medial to it on the posterior arm surface. The medial head can be exposed by transecting the lateral head and pulling it aside. Now pull on the triceps muscle.

How does the function of the triceps muscle compare in cats and in humans?

_____

_____

Anterior and distal to the medial head of the triceps is the tiny **anconeus** muscle (not visible in Figure 8), sometimes called the fourth head of the triceps muscle. Notice its darker color and the way it wraps the tip of the elbow.

2. The **brachialis** can be located anterior to the lateral head of the triceps muscle. Identify its origin on the humerus, and trace its course as it crosses the elbow and inserts on the ulna. It flexes the cat's foreleg.

Identification of the forearm muscles is difficult because of the tough fascia sheath that encases them, but give it a try.

9

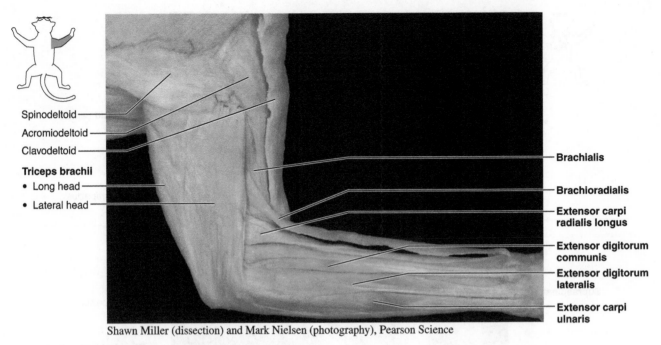

Spinodeltoid

Acromiodeltoid

Clavodeltoid

Triceps brachii
- Long head
- Lateral head

Brachialis

Brachioradialis

Extensor carpi radialis longus

Extensor digitorum communis

Extensor digitorum lateralis

Extensor carpi ulnaris

Shawn Miller (dissection) and Mark Nielsen (photography), Pearson Science

FIGURE 8 Lateral surface of the forelimb of the cat.

3. Remove as much of the connective tissue as possible and cut through the ligaments that secure the tendons at the wrist (transverse carpal ligaments) so that you will be able to follow the muscles to their insertions. Begin your identification of the forearm muscles at the lateral surface of the forearm. The muscles of this region are very much alike in appearance and are difficult to identify accurately unless a definite order is followed. Thus you will begin with the most anterior muscles and proceed to the posterior aspect. Remember to check carefully the tendons of insertion to verify your muscle identifications.

4. The ribbonlike muscle on the lateral surface of the humerus is the **brachioradialis.** Observe how it passes down the forearm to insert on the styloid process of the radius. (If your removal of the fascia was not very careful, this muscle may have been removed.)

5. The **extensor carpi radialis longus** has a broad origin and is larger than the brachioradialis. It extends down the anterior surface of the radius (see Figure 8). Transect this muscle to view the **extensor carpi radialis brevis,** which is partially covered by and sometimes fused with the extensor carpi radialis longus. Both muscles have origins, insertions, and actions similar to their human counterparts.

6. You can see the entire **extensor digitorum communis** along the lateral surface of the forearm. Trace it to its four tendons, which insert on the second to fifth digits. This muscle extends these digits. The **extensor digitorum lateralis** (absent in humans) also extends the digits. This muscle lies immediately posterior to the extensor digitorum communis.

7. Follow the **extensor carpi ulnaris** from the lateral epicondyle of the humerus to the ulnar side of the fifth metacarpal. Often this muscle has a shiny tendon, which helps in its identification.

Muscles of the Medial Surface

1. The **biceps brachii** (Figure 9) is a large spindle-shaped muscle medial to the brachialis on the anterior surface of the humerus. Pull back the cut ends of the pectoral muscles to get a good view of the biceps. This muscle is much more prominent in humans, but its origin, insertion, and action are very similar in cats and in humans. Follow the muscle to its origin.

Does the biceps have two heads in the cat? _____

2. The broad, flat, exceedingly thin muscle on the posteromedial surface of the arm is the **epitrochlearis.** Its tendon originates from the fascia of the latissimus dorsi, and the muscle inserts into the olecranon process of the ulna. This muscle extends the forearm of the cat; it is not found in humans.

3. The **coracobrachialis** (not illustrated) of the cat is insignificant (approximately 1.3 cm, or ½ inch, long) and can be seen as a very small muscle crossing the ventral aspect of the shoulder joint. It runs beneath the biceps brachii to insert on the humerus and has the same function as the human coracobrachialis.

4. Referring again to Figure 9, turn the cat so that the ventral forearm muscles (mostly flexors and pronators) can be observed. As in humans, most of these muscles arise from the medial epicondyle of the humerus. The **pronator teres** runs from the medial epicondyle of the humerus and declines in size as it approaches its insertion on the radius. Do not bother to trace it to its insertion.

5. Like its human counterpart, the **flexor carpi radialis** runs from the medial epicondyle of the humerus to insert into the second and third metacarpals.

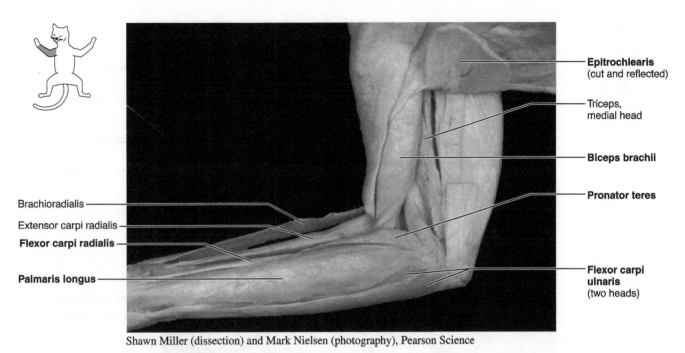

Shawn Miller (dissection) and Mark Nielsen (photography), Pearson Science

FIGURE 9 Medial surface of the forelimb of the cat.

6.   The large flat muscle in the center of the medial surface is the **palmaris longus.** Its origin on the medial epicondyle of the humerus abuts that of the pronator teres and is shared with the flexor carpi radialis. The palmaris longus extends down the forearm to terminate in four tendons on the digits. This muscle is proportionately larger in cats than in humans.

The **flexor carpi ulnaris** arises from a two-headed origin (medial epicondyle of the humerus and olecranon of the ulna). Its two bellies pass downward to the wrist, where they are united by a single tendon that inserts into the carpals of the wrist. As in humans, this muscle flexes the wrist. ▬

ACTIVITY 4

Dissecting Hindlimb Muscles

Remove the fat and fascia from all thigh surfaces, but do not cut through or remove the **fascia lata** (or iliotibial band), which is a tough white aponeurosis covering the anterolateral surface of the thigh from the hip to the leg. If the cat is a male, the cord-like sperm duct will be embedded in the fat near the pubic symphysis. Carefully clear around, but not in, this region.

Posterolateral Hindlimb Muscles

1.   Turn the cat on its ventral surface and identify the following superficial muscles of the hip and thigh, referring to Figure 10. Viewing the lateral aspect of the hindlimb, you will identify these muscles in sequence from the anterior to the posterior aspects of the hip and thigh. Most anterior is the **sartorius** seen in this view as a thin band. Approximately 4 cm (1½ inches) wide, it extends around the lateral aspect of the thigh to the anterior surface, where the major portion of it lies (see Figure 12a). Free it from the adjacent muscles and pass a blunt probe under it to trace its origin and insertion.

Homologous to the sartorius muscle in humans, it adducts and rotates the thigh, but in addition, the cat sartorius acts as a knee extensor. Transect this muscle.

2.   The **tensor fasciae latae** is posterior to the sartorius. It is wide at its superior end, where it originates on the iliac crest, and narrows as it approaches its insertion into the fascia lata, which runs to the proximal tibial region. Transect its superior end and pull it back to expose the **gluteus medius** lying beneath it. This is the largest of the gluteus muscles in the cat. It originates on the ilium and inserts on the greater trochanter of the femur. The gluteus medius overlays and obscures the gluteus minimus, pyriformis, and gemellus muscles (which will not be identified here).

3.   The **gluteus maximus** is a small triangular hip muscle posterior to the superior end of the tensor fasciae latae and paralleling it. In humans the gluteus maximus is a large fleshy muscle forming most of the buttock mass. In the cat it is only about 1.3 cm (½ inch) wide and 5 cm (2 inches) long, and is smaller than the gluteus medius. The gluteus maximus covers part of the gluteus medius as it extends from the sacral region to the end of the femur. It abducts the thigh.

4.   Posterior to the gluteus maximus, identify the triangular **caudofemoralis,** which originates on the caudal vertebrae and inserts into the patella via an aponeurosis. There is no homologue to this muscle in humans; in cats it abducts the thigh and flexes the vertebral column.

5.   The **hamstring muscles** of the hindlimb include the biceps femoris, the semitendinosus, and the semimembranosus muscles. The **biceps femoris** is a large, powerful muscle that covers about three-fourths of the posterolateral surface of the thigh. It is 4 cm (1½ inches) to 5 cm (2 inches) wide throughout its length. Trace it from its origin on the ischial tuberosity to its insertion on the tibia. Part of the **semitendinosus** can be

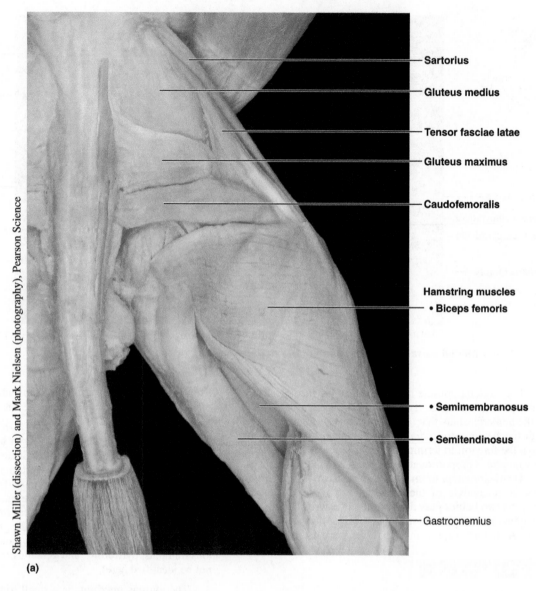

Sartorius

Gluteus medius

Tensor fasciae latae

Gluteus maximus

Caudofemoralis

Hamstring muscles
• Biceps femoris

• Semimembranosus

• Semitendinosus

Gastrocnemius

Shawn Miller (dissection) and Mark Nielsen (photography), Pearson Science

(a)

FIGURE 10 Muscles of the posterolateral thigh in the cat. (a) Superficial view.

seen beneath the posterior border of the biceps femoris. Transect and reflect the biceps muscle to reveal the whole length of the semitendinosus and the large sciatic nerve positioned under the biceps (Figure 10b). Contrary to what its name implies ("half-tendon"), this muscle is muscular and fleshy except at its insertion. It is uniformly about 2 cm (¾ inch) wide as it runs down the thigh from the ischial tuberosity to the medial side of the tibia. It bends the knee. The **semimembranosus,** a large muscle lying medial to the semitendinosus and largely obscured by it, is best seen in an anterior view of the thigh (see Figure 12b). If desired, however, the semitendinosus can be transected to view it from the posterior aspect. The semimembranosus is larger and broader than the semitendinosus. Like the other hamstrings, it originates on the ischial tuberosity and inserts on the medial epicondyle of the femur and the medial tibial surface.

How does the semimembranosus compare with its human homologue?

_____

_____

6. Remove the heavy fascia covering the lateral surface of the shank (leg). Moving from the posterior to the anterior aspect, identify the following muscles on the posterolateral shank (Figure 11). First reflect the lower portion of the biceps femoris to see the origin of the **triceps surae,** the large composite muscle of the calf. Humans also have a triceps surae. The **gastrocnemius,** part of the triceps surae, is the largest muscle on the shank. As in humans, it has two heads and inserts via the calcaneal (Achilles) tendon into the calcaneus. Run a probe beneath this muscle and then transect it to reveal the **soleus,** which is deep to the gastrocnemius.

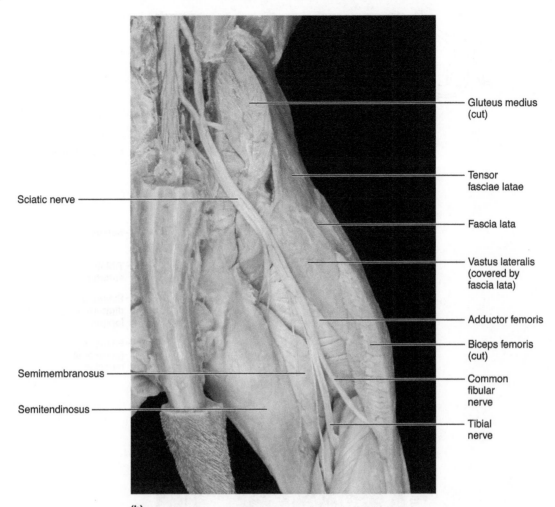

(b)

Shawn Miller (dissection) and Mark Nielsen (photography), Pearson Science

FIGURE 10 *(continued)* **(b)** Deep muscles.

7.   Another important group of muscles in the leg is the **fibularis (peroneus) muscles,** which collectively appear as a slender, evenly shaped superficial muscle lying anterior to the triceps surae. Originating on the fibula and inserting on the digits and metatarsals, the fibularis muscles flex the foot.

8.   The **extensor digitorum longus** lies anterior to the fibularis muscles. Its origin, insertion, and action in cats are similar to the homologous human muscle. The **tibialis anterior** is anterior to the extensor digitorum longus. The tibialis anterior is roughly triangular in cross section and heavier at its proximal end. Locate its origin on the proximal fibula and tibia and its insertion on the first metatarsal. You can see the sharp edge of the tibia at the anterior border of this muscle. As in humans, it is a foot flexor.

Anteromedial Hindlimb Muscles

1.   Turn the cat onto its dorsal surface to identify the muscles of the anteromedial hindlimb (Figure 12). Note once again the straplike sartorius at the surface of the thigh, which you have already identified and transected. It originates on the ilium and inserts on the medial region of the tibia.

2.   Reflect the cut ends of the sartorius to identify the **quadriceps** muscles. The most medial muscle of this group, the **vastus medialis,** lies just beneath the sartorius. Resting close to the femur, it arises from the ilium and inserts into the patellar ligament. The small spindle-shaped muscle anterior and lateral to the vastus medialis is the **rectus femoris.** In cats this muscle originates entirely from the femur.

What is the origin of the rectus femoris in humans?

_____

Free the rectus femoris from the most lateral muscle of this group, the large, fleshy **vastus lateralis,** which lies deep to the tensor fasciae latae. The vastus lateralis arises from the lateral femoral surface and inserts, along with the other vasti muscles, into the patellar ligament. Transect this muscle to identify the deep **vastus intermedius,** the smallest of the vasti muscles. It lies medial to the vastus lateralis and merges superiorly with the vastus medialis. (The vastus intermedius is not shown in the figure.)

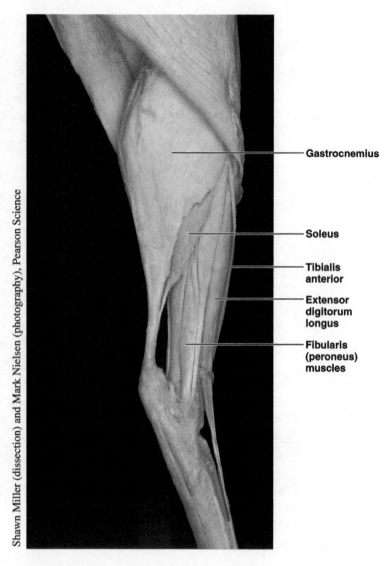

Shawn Miller (dissection) and Mark Nielsen (photography), Pearson Science

- Gastrocnemius
- Soleus
- Tibialis anterior
- Extensor digitorum longus
- Fibularis (peroneus) muscles

FIGURE 11 Superficial muscles of the posterolateral aspect of the shank (leg).

3. The **gracilis** is a broad thin muscle that covers the posterior portion of the medial aspect of the thigh (see Figure 12a). It originates on the pubic symphysis and inserts on the medial proximal tibial surface. In cats the gracilis adducts the leg and draws it posteriorly.

How does this compare with the human gracilis?

_____

_____

4. Free and transect the gracilis to view the adductor muscles deep to it. The **adductor femoris** is a large muscle that lies beneath the gracilis and abuts the semimembranosus medially. Its origin is the pubic ramus and the ischium, and its fibers pass downward to insert on most of the length of the femoral shaft. The adductor femoris is homologous to the human *adductor magnus, brevis,* and *longus.* Its function is to extend the thigh after it has been drawn forward, and to adduct the thigh. A small muscle about 2.5 cm (1 inch) long— the **adductor longus**—touches the superior margin of the adductor femoris. It originates on the pubic bone and inserts on the proximal surface of the femur.

5. Before continuing your dissection, locate the **femoral triangle** (Scarpa's triangle), an important area bordered by the proximal edge of the sartorius and the adductor muscles. It is usually possible to identify the femoral artery (injected with red latex) and the femoral vein (injected with blue latex), which span the triangle (see Figure 12a). (You will identify these vessels again in your study of the circulatory system.) If your instructor wishes you to identify the pectineus and iliopsoas, remove these vessels and go on to steps 6 and 7.

6. Examine the superolateral margin of the adductor longus to locate the small **pectineus.** It is sometimes covered by the gracilis (which you have cut and reflected). The pectineus, which originates on the pubis and inserts on the proximal end of the femur, is similar in all ways to its human homologue.

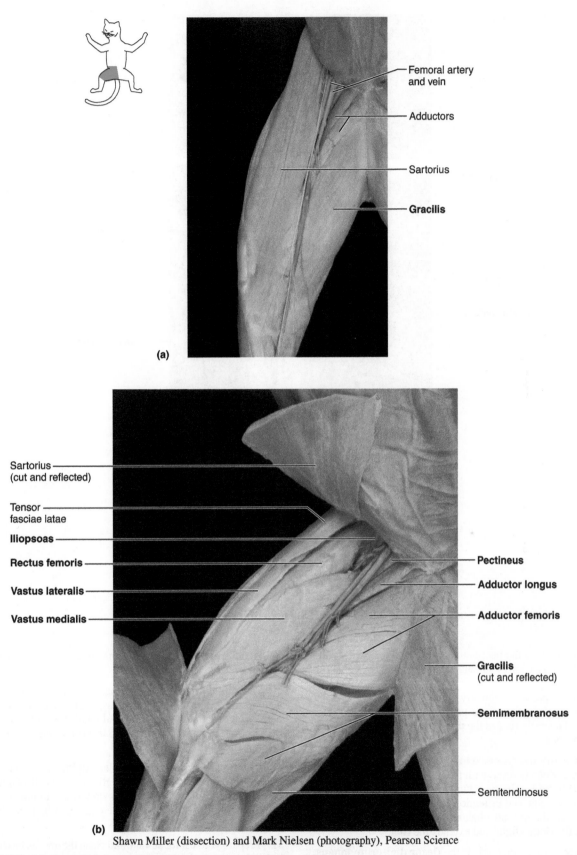

Femoral artery
and vein

Adductors

Sartorius

Gracilis

(a)

Sartorius
(cut and reflected)

Tensor
fasciae latae

Iliopsoas

Rectus femoris

Vastus lateralis

Vastus medialis

Pectineus

Adductor longus

Adductor femoris

Gracilis
(cut and reflected)

Semimembranosus

Semitendinosus

(b)

Shawn Miller (dissection) and Mark Nielsen (photography), Pearson Science

FIGURE 12 Superficial muscles of the anteromedial thigh. (a) Gracilis and
sartorius are intact in this superficial view of the right thigh. **(b)** The gracilis and sartorius
are transected and reflected to show deeper muscles.

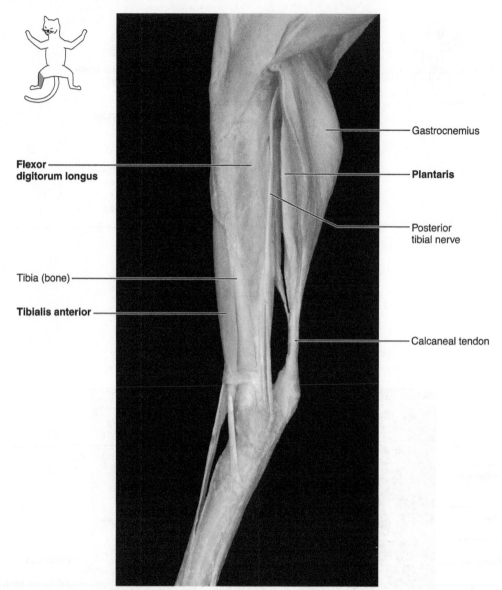

Shawn Miller (dissection) and Mark Nielsen (photography), Pearson Science

FIGURE 13 Superficial muscles of the anteromedial shank (leg) of the cat.

7. Just lateral to the pectineus you can see a small portion of the **iliopsoas,** a long and cylindrical muscle. Its origin is on the transverse processes of T_1 through T_{12} and the lumbar vertebrae, and it passes posteriorly toward the body wall to insert on the medial aspect of the proximal femur. The iliopsoas flexes and laterally rotates the thigh. It corresponds to the human iliopsoas.

8. Reidentify the gastrocnemius of the shank and then the **plantaris,** which is fused with the lateral head of the gastrocnemius (Figure 13). It originates from the lateral aspect of the femur and patella, and its tendon passes around the calcaneus to insert on the second phalanx. Working with the triceps surae, it flexes the digits and extends the foot.

9. Anterior to the plantaris is the **flexor digitorum longus,** a long, tapering muscle with two heads. It originates on the lateral surfaces of the proximal fibula and tibia and inserts via four tendons into the terminal phalanges. As in humans, it flexes the toes.

10. The **tibialis posterior** is a long, flat muscle lateral and deep to the flexor digitorum longus. It originates on the medial surface of the head of the fibula and the ventral tibia. It merges with a flat, shiny tendon to insert into the tarsals. It is not shown in the figure.

11. The **flexor hallucis longus** (also not illustrated) is a long muscle that lies lateral to the tibialis posterior. It originates from the posterior tibia and passes downward to the ankle. It is a uniformly broad muscle in the cat. As in humans, it is a flexor of the great toe.

12. Prepare your cat for storage and clean the area as instructed before leaving the laboratory. ■

Many human muscles are modified from those of the cat (or any quadruped) as a result of the requirements of an upright posture. The following questions refer to these differences.

1. How does the human trapezius muscle differ from the cat's?

   _____

   _____

2. How does the deltoid differ?

   _____

   _____

3. How do the size and orientation of the human gluteus muscle differ from that in the cat?

   _____

   _____

4. Explain these differences in terms of differences in function.

   _____

   _____

5. The human rectus abdominis is definitely divided by four transverse tendons (tendinous intersections). These tendons are absent or difficult to identify in the cat. How do these tendons affect the human upright posture?

   _____

   _____

6. Match each term in column B to its description in column A.

   Column A   **Column B**

   _____ 1. to separate muscles   a. dissect

   _____ 2. to fold back a muscle   b. embalm

   _____ 3. to cut through a muscle   c. reflect

   _____ 4. to preserve tissue   d. transect

Dissection of Cat Spinal Nerves

MATERIALS

☐ Disposable gloves
☐ Dissecting instruments and tray
☐ Animal specimen from previous dissection
☐ Embalming fluid
☐ Paper towels

OBJECTIVE

To identify on a dissected animal the musculocutaneous, radial, median, and ulnar nerves of the forelimb and the femoral, saphenous, sciatic, common fibular (peroneal), and tibial nerves of the hindlimb.

The cat has 38 or 39 pairs of spinal nerves (as compared to 31 in humans). Of these, 8 are cervical, 13 thoracic, 7 lumbar, 3 sacral, and 7 or 8 caudal. A complete dissection of the cat's spinal nerves would be extraordinarily time-consuming and exacting and is not warranted in a basic anatomy and physiology course. However, it is desirable for you to have some dissection work to complement your study of the anatomical charts. Thus at this point you will carry out a partial dissection of the brachial plexus and lumbosacral plexus and identify some of the major nerves.

ACTIVITY 1

Dissecting Nerves of the Brachial Plexus

1. Don disposable gloves. Place your cat specimen on the dissecting tray, dorsal side down. Reflect the cut ends of the left pectoralis muscles to expose the large brachial plexus in the axillary region (Figure 1). Use forceps to carefully clear away the connective tissue around the exposed nerves as far back toward their points of origin as possible.

2. The **musculocutaneous nerve** is the most superior nerve of this group. It splits into two subdivisions that run under the margins of the coracobrachialis and biceps brachii muscles. Trace its fibers into the ventral muscles of the arm it serves.

3. Locate the large **radial nerve** inferior to the musculocutaneous nerve. The radial nerve serves the dorsal muscles of the arm and forearm. Follow it into the three heads of the triceps brachii muscle.

PAL

For access to anatomical models and more, check out Practice Anatomy Lab.

From Dissection Exercise 2 of *Human Anatomy & Physiology Laboratory Manual, PhysioEx 9.0 Update, Cat Version*, Tenth Edition.
Elaine N. Marieb, Susan J. Mitchell. Copyright © 2012 by Pearson Education, Inc. Published by Pearson Benjamin Cummings. All rights reserved.

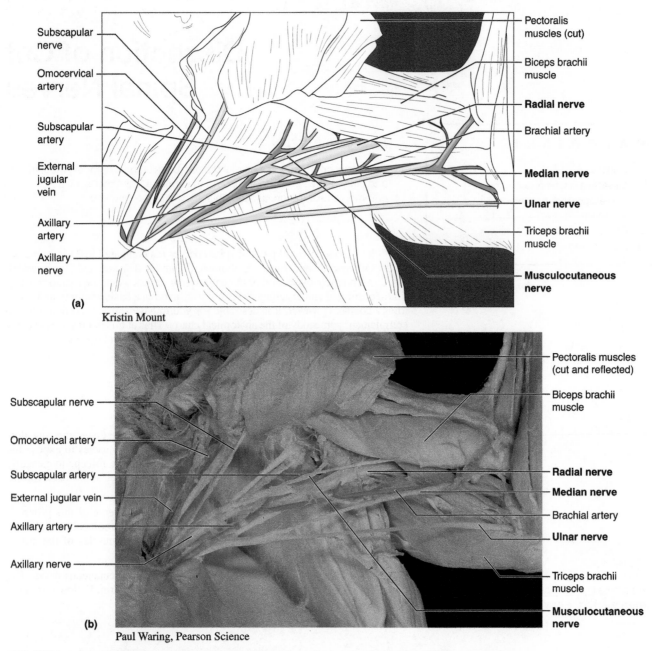

Subscapular nerve

Omocervical artery

Subscapular artery

External jugular vein

Axillary artery

Axillary nerve

Pectoralis muscles (cut)

Biceps brachii muscle

Radial nerve

Brachial artery

Median nerve

Ulnar nerve

Triceps brachii muscle

Musculocutaneous nerve

(a)

Kristin Mount

Subscapular nerve

Omocervical artery

Subscapular artery

External jugular vein

Axillary artery

Axillary nerve

Pectoralis muscles (cut and reflected)

Biceps brachii muscle

Radial nerve

Median nerve

Brachial artery

Ulnar nerve

Triceps brachii muscle

Musculocutaneous nerve

(b)

Paul Waring, Pearson Science

FIGURE 1 Brachial plexus and major blood vessels of the left forelimb of the cat, ventral aspect. (a) Diagrammatic view. **(b)** Photograph.

4. In the cat, the **median nerve** is closely associated with the brachial artery and vein (see Figure 1). It courses through the arm to supply the ventral muscles of the forearm (with the exception of the flexor carpi ulnaris and the ulnar head of the flexor digitorum profundus). It also innervates some of the intrinsic hand muscles, as in humans. Locate and follow it to the ventral forearm muscles.

5. The **ulnar nerve** is the most posterior of the large brachial plexus nerves. Follow it as it travels down the forelimb, passing over the medial epicondyle of the humerus, to supply the flexor carpi ulnaris and the ulnar head of the flexor digitorum profundus (and the hand muscles). ▬

ACTIVITY 2

Dissecting Nerves of the Lumbosacral Plexus

1. To locate the **femoral nerve** arising from the lumbar plexus, first identify the *femoral triangle,* which is bordered by the sartorius and adductor muscles of the anterior thigh (Figure 2). The large femoral nerve travels through this region after emerging from the psoas major muscle in close association with the femoral artery and vein. Follow the nerve into the muscles and skin of the anterior thigh, which it supplies. Notice also its cutaneous branch in the cat, the **saphenous nerve,** which continues down the anterior medial

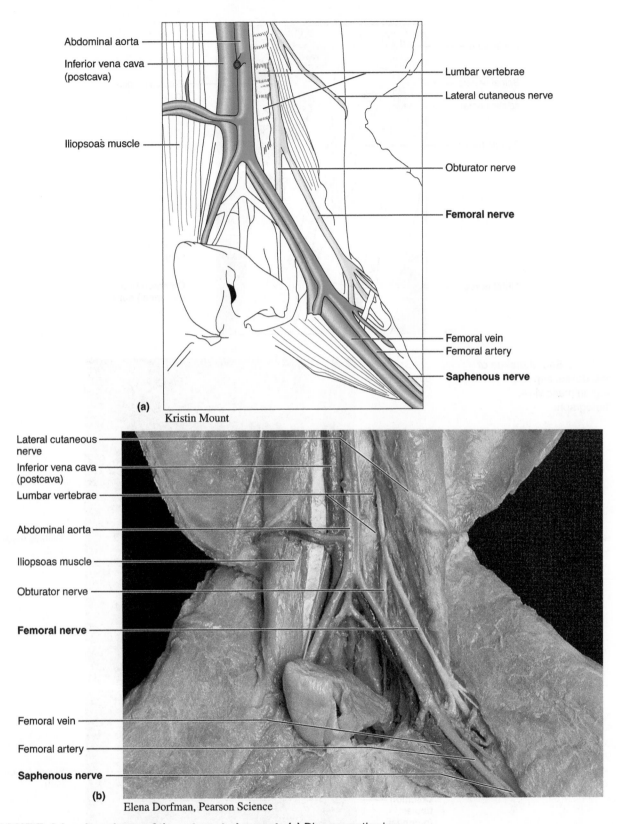

(a)

Kristin Mount

Abdominal aorta
Inferior vena cava (postcava)
Iliopsoas muscle
Lumbar vertebrae
Lateral cutaneous nerve
Obturator nerve
Femoral nerve
Femoral vein
Femoral artery
Saphenous nerve

(b)

Elena Dorfman, Pearson Science

Lateral cutaneous nerve
Inferior vena cava (postcava)
Lumbar vertebrae
Abdominal aorta
Iliopsoas muscle
Obturator nerve
Femoral nerve
Femoral vein
Femoral artery
Saphenous nerve

FIGURE 2 Lumbar plexus of the cat, ventral aspect. (a) Diagrammatic view.
(b) Photograph.

Dissection of Cat Spinal Nerves

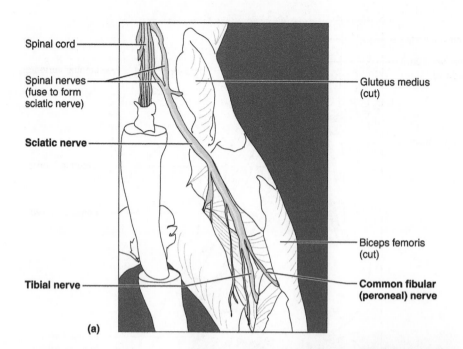

Spinal cord

Spinal nerves
(fuse to form
sciatic nerve)

Sciatic nerve

Tibial nerve

Gluteus medius
(cut)

Biceps femoris
(cut)

**Common fibular
(peroneal) nerve**

(a)

**FIGURE 3 Sacral plexus of
the cat, dorsal aspect.**
(a) Diagrammatic view.
(b) Photograph.

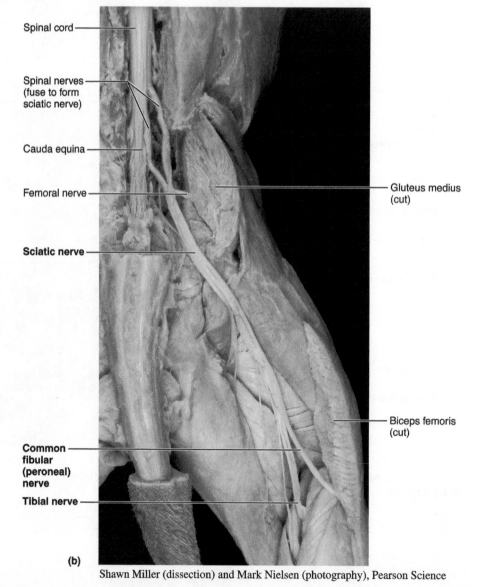

Spinal cord

Spinal nerves
(fuse to form
sciatic nerve)

Cauda equina

Femoral nerve

Sciatic nerve

Gluteus medius
(cut)

Biceps femoris
(cut)

**Common
fibular
(peroneal)
nerve**

Tibial nerve

(b)

Shawn Miller (dissection) and Mark Nielsen (photography), Pearson Science

surface of the thigh (with the great saphenous artery and vein) to supply the skin of the anterior shank and foot.

2.   Turn the cat ventral side down so you can view the posterior aspect of the lower limb (Figure 3). Reflect the ends of the transected biceps femoris muscle to view the large cord-like sciatic nerve. The **sciatic nerve** arises from the sacral plexus and serves the dorsal thigh muscles and all the muscles of the leg and foot. Follow the nerve as it travels down the posterior thigh lateral to the semimembranosus muscle. Note

that just superior to the gastrocnemius muscle of the calf, it divides into its two major branches, which serve the leg.

3.   Identify the **tibial nerve** medially and the **common fibular (peroneal) nerve,** which curves over the lateral surface of the gastrocnemius.

4.   When you have finished making your observations, wrap the cat for storage and clean all dissecting tools and equipment before leaving the laboratory. ▬

DISSECTION REVIEW

1.   From anterior to posterior, put in their proper order the nerves issuing from the brachial plexus (i.e., the median, musculo-cutaneous, radial, and ulnar nerves).

_____

_____

2.   Which of the nerves named above serves the cat's forearm extensor muscles? _____ Which serves the forearm

flexors? _____

3.   Just superior to the gastrocnemius muscle, the sciatic nerve divides into its two main branches, the _____

and _____ nerves.

4.   What name is given to the cutaneous nerve of the cat's thigh? _____

Identification of Selected Endocrine Organs of the Cat

MATERIALS

- ☐ Plastic gloves
- ☐ Dissection instruments and tray
- ☐ Animal specimen from previous dissections
- ☐ Bone cutters
- ☐ Embalming fluid
- ☐ Paper towels

OBJECTIVES

1. To prepare the cat for observation by opening the ventral body cavity.
2. To identify and name the major endocrine organs on a dissected cat.

ACTIVITY 1

Opening the Ventral Body Cavity

1.   Don gloves and then obtain your dissection animal. Place the animal on the dissecting tray, ventral side up. Using scissors, make a longitudinal median incision through the ventral body wall. Begin your cut just superior to the midline of the pubic bone and continue it anteriorly to the rib cage. Check the incision guide provided in Figure 1 as you work along.

2.   Angle the scissors slightly (1.3 cm, or ½ inch) to the right or left of the sternum, and continue the cut through the rib cartilages (just lateral to the body

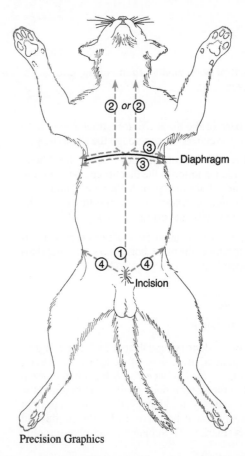

Precision Graphics

FIGURE 1 Incisions to be made in opening the ventral body cavity of a cat. Numbers indicate sequence.

PAL

For access to anatomical models and more, check out Practice Anatomy Lab.

From Dissection Exercise 3 of *Human Anatomy & Physiology Laboratory Manual, PhysioEx 9.0 Update, Cat Version*, Tenth Edition.
Elaine N. Marieb, Susan J. Mitchell. Copyright © 2012 by Pearson Education, Inc. Published by Pearson Benjamin Cummings. All rights reserved.

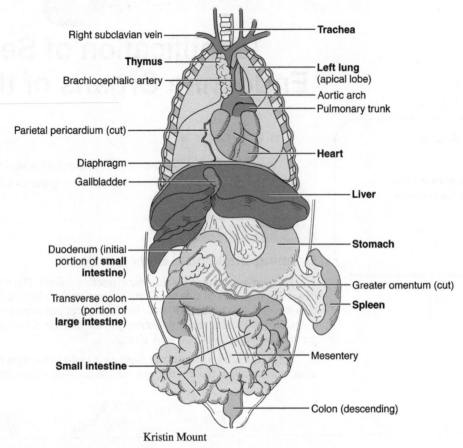

Right subclavian vein

Thymus

Brachiocephalic artery

Parietal pericardium (cut)

Diaphragm

Gallbladder

Duodenum (initial portion of **small intestine**)

Transverse colon (portion of **large intestine**)

Small intestine

Trachea

Left lung (apical lobe)

Aortic arch

Pulmonary trunk

Heart

Liver

Stomach

Greater omentum (cut)

Spleen

Mesentery

Colon (descending)

Kristin Mount

FIGURE 2 Ventral body cavity organs of the cat. Superficial view with greater omentum removed.

midline), to the base of the throat. Your instructor may have you use heavier bone cutters to cut through the rib cartilages.

3. Make two lateral cuts on both sides of the ventral body surface, anterior and posterior to the diaphragm, which separates the thoracic and abdominal parts of the ventral body cavity. *Leave the diaphragm intact.* Spread the thoracic walls laterally to expose the thoracic organs.

4. Make an angled lateral cut on each side of the median incision line just superior to the pubic bone, and spread the flaps to expose the abdominal cavity organs. ▇

ACTIVITY 2

Identifying Organs

A helpful adjunct to identifying selected endocrine organs of the cat is a general overview of ventral body cavity organs as shown in Figure 2. Since you will study the organ systems housed in the ventral body cavity in later units, the objective here is simply to identify the most important organs and those that will help you to locate the desired endocrine organs (marked *). Schematic and photographic

cat images showing the relative positioning of several of the animal's endocrine organs are provided in Figure 3.

Before leaving the lab, prepare your animal for storage as instructed. Then clean and dry all dissecting equipment, wash down your lab bench, and properly dispose of your gloves.

Neck and Thoracic Cavity Organs

Trachea: The windpipe; runs down the midline of the throat and then divides just anterior to the lungs to form the bronchi, which plunge into the lungs on either side.

***Thyroid:** Its dark lobes straddle the trachea (see Figure 3b). This endocrine organ's hormones are the main hormones regulating the body's metabolic rate.

***Thymus:** Glandular structure superior to and partly covering the heart (see Figure 3b). The thymus is intimately involved (via its hormones) in programming the immune system. If you have a young cat, the thymus will be quite large. In old cats, most of this organ has been replaced by fat.

Heart: In the mediastinum enclosed by the pericardium.

Lungs: Paired organs flanking the heart.

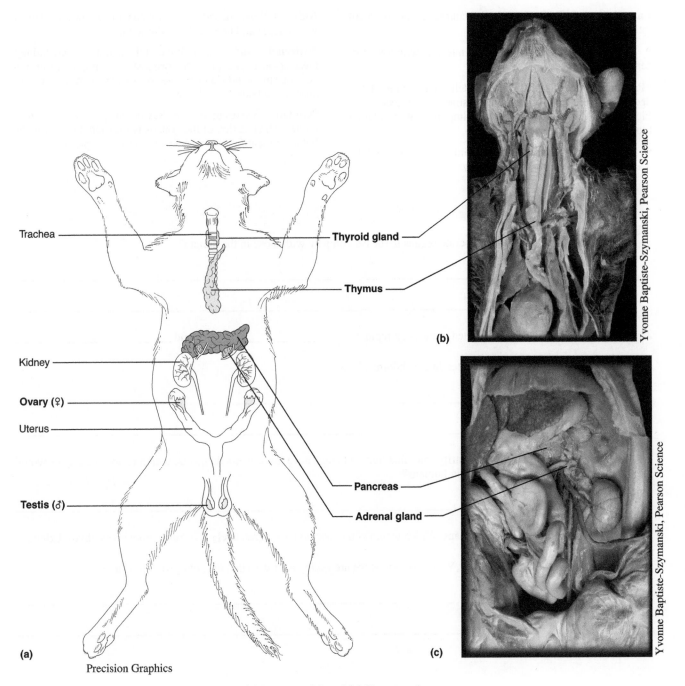

Trachea

Kidney

Ovary (♀)

Uterus

Testis (♂)

Thyroid gland

Thymus

Pancreas

Adrenal gland

(a)

(b)

(c)

Precision Graphics

Yvonne Baptiste-Szymanski, Pearson Science

FIGURE 3 **Endocrine organs in the cat.** **(a)** Drawing. **(b)** and **(c)** Photographs.

Abdominal Cavity Organs

Liver: Large multilobed organ lying under the umbrella of the diaphragm.

- Lift the drapelike, fat-infiltrated greater omentum covering the abdominal organs to expose the following organs:

Stomach: Dorsally located sac to the left side of the liver.

Spleen: Flattened brown organ curving around the lateral aspect of the stomach.

Small intestine: Tubelike organ continuing posteriorly from the stomach.

Large intestine: Taking a U-shaped course around the small intestine to terminate in the rectum.

- Lift the first section of the small intestine with your forceps to see the pancreas.

*Pancreas: Diffuse gland located in delicate mesentery lying deep to and between the small intestine and stomach (see Figure 3c). This gland is extremely important in regulating blood sugar levels.

- Push the intestines to one side with a probe to reveal the deeper organs in the abdominal cavity.

Kidneys: Bean-shaped organs located toward the dorsal body wall surface and behind the peritoneum.

*Adrenal glands: Seen above and medial to each kidney, these small glands produce corticosteroids important in preventing stress and abnormalities of water and electrolyte balance in the body (see Figure 3c).

*Gonads (ovaries or testes): Sex organs producing sex hormones. The location of the gonads is illustrated in Figure 3a, but their identification is deferred until the reproductive system organs are considered. ■

DISSECTION REVIEW

1. How do the locations of the endocrine organs in the cat compare with those in the human?

_____

_____

2. Name two endocrine organs located in the neck region: _____ and _____

3. Name three endocrine organs located in the abdominal cavity.

_____

_____

4. Given the assumption (not necessarily true) that human beings have more stress than cats, which endocrine organs would you expect to be relatively larger in humans?

_____

5. Cats are smaller animals than humans. Which would you expect to have a (relatively speaking) more active thyroid gland—

cats or humans? _____ Why? (We know we are asking a lot with this one, but give it a whirl.)

_____

_____

Dissection of the Blood Vessels of the Cat

MATERIALS

- ☐ Disposable gloves
- ☐ Dissecting instruments and tray
- ☐ Animal specimen from previous dissections
- ☐ Bone cutters
- ☐ Scissors
- ☐ Embalming fluid
- ☐ Paper towels

OBJECTIVES

1. To identify some of the most important blood vessels of the cat.
2. To point out anatomical differences between the vascular system of the human and the cat.

ACTIVITY 1

Opening the Ventral Body Cavity

If you have already opened your animal's ventral body cavity and identified many of its organs, begin this exercise with Activity 3 (Preparing to Identify the Blood Vessels).

If not, open the ventral body cavity. ▬

ACTIVITY 2

Preliminary Organ Identification

A helpful prelude to identifying and tracing the blood supply of the various organs of the cat is a preliminary identification of ventral body cavity organs shown in Figure 1. Since you will study the organ systems contained in the ventral cavity in later units, the objective here is simply to identify the most important organs. Using Figure 1 as a guide, identify the following body cavity organs:

Thoracic Cavity Organs

Heart: In the mediastinum enclosed by the pericardium.

Lungs: Flanking the heart.

Thymus: Superior to and partially covering the heart. The thymus is quite large in young cats but is largely replaced by fat as cats age.

Abdominal Cavity Organs

Liver: Posterior to the diaphragm.

- Lift the large, drapelike, fat-infiltrated greater omentum covering the abdominal organs to expose the following:

Stomach: Dorsally located and to the left of the liver.

Spleen: A flattened, brown organ curving around the lateral aspect of the stomach.

Small intestine: Continuing posteriorly from the stomach.

Large intestine: Taking a U-shaped course around the small intestine and terminating in the rectum. ▬

PAL

For access to anatomical models and more, check out Practice Anatomy Lab.

From Dissection Exercise 4 of *Human Anatomy & Physiology Laboratory Manual, PhysioEx 9.0 Update, Cat Version*, Tenth Edition. Elaine N. Marieb, Susan J. Mitchell. Copyright © 2012 by Pearson Education, Inc. Published by Pearson Benjamin Cummings. All rights reserved.

Dissection of the Blood Vessels of the Cat

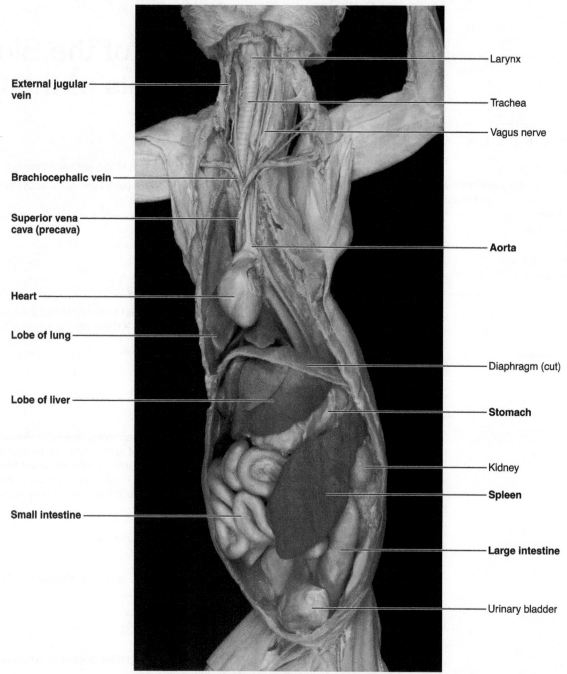

External jugular vein

Brachiocephalic vein

Superior vena cava (precava)

Heart

Lobe of lung

Lobe of liver

Small intestine

Larynx

Trachea

Vagus nerve

Aorta

Diaphragm (cut)

Stomach

Kidney

Spleen

Large intestine

Urinary bladder

Shawn Miller (dissection) and Mark Nielsen (photography), Pearson Science

FIGURE 1 Ventral body cavity organs of the cat. (Greater omentum has been removed.)

ACTIVITY 3

Preparing to Identify the Blood Vessels

1.   Carefully clear away any thymus tissue or fat obscuring the heart and the large vessels associated with the heart. Before identifying the blood vessels, try to locate the *phrenic nerve* (from the cervical plexus), which innervates the diaphragm. The phrenic nerves lie ventral to the root of the lung on each side, as they pass to the diaphragm. Also attempt to

locate the *vagus nerve* (cranial nerve X) passing laterally along the trachea and dorsal to the root of the lung.

2.   Slit the parietal pericardium and reflect it superiorly. Then, cut it away from its heart attachments. Review the structures of the heart. Notice its pointed inferior end (apex) and its broader superior portion. Identify the two *atria,* which appear darker than the inferior *ventricles.*

3.   Identify the **aorta,** the largest artery in the body, issuing from the left ventricle. Also identify the *coronary arteries* in the sulcus on the ventral surface of the heart; these should be

injected with red latex. As an aid to blood vessel identification, the arteries of laboratory dissection specimens are injected with red latex; the veins are injected with blue latex. Exceptions to this will be noted as they are encountered.

4. Identify the two large venae cavae—the **superior and inferior venae cavae**—entering the right atrium. The superior vena cava is the largest dark-colored vessel entering the base of the heart. These vessels are called the precava and postcava, respectively, in the cat. The caval veins drain the same relative body areas as in humans. Also identify the **pulmonary trunk** (usually injected with blue latex) extending anteriorly from the right ventricle and the right and left pulmonary arteries. Trace the **pulmonary arteries** until they enter the lungs. Locate the **pulmonary veins** entering the left atrium and the ascending aorta arising from the left ventricle and running dorsal to the precava and to the left of the body midline. ▬

ACTIVITY 4

Identifying the Arteries of the Cat

Refer to Figure 2 and to the summary photo in Figure 5 as you study the arterial system of the cat.

1. Reidentify the aorta as it emerges from the left ventricle. As you observed in the dissection of the sheep heart, the first branches of the aorta are the **coronary arteries,** which supply the myocardium. The coronary arteries emerge from the base of the aorta and can be seen on the surface of the heart. Follow the aorta as it arches (aortic arch), and identify its major branches. In the cat, the aortic arch gives off two large vessels, the **brachiocephalic artery** and the **left subclavian artery.** The brachiocephalic artery has three major branches, the right subclavian artery and the right and left common carotid arteries. (Note that in humans, the left common carotid artery and left subclavian artery are direct branches off the aortic arch.)

2. Follow the **right common carotid artery** along the right side of the trachea as it moves anteriorly, giving off branches to the neck muscles, thyroid gland, and trachea. At the level of the larynx, it branches to form the **external** and **internal carotid arteries.** The internal carotid is quite small in the cat and it may be difficult to locate. It may even be absent. The distribution of the carotid arteries parallels that in humans.

3. Follow the **right subclavian artery** laterally. It gives off four branches, the first being the tiny **vertebral artery,** which along with the internal carotid artery provides the arterial circulation of the brain. Other branches of the subclavian artery include the **costocervical trunk** (to the costal and cervical regions), the **thyrocervical trunk** (to the shoulder), and the **internal thoracic (mammary) artery** (serving the ventral thoracic wall). As the subclavian passes in front of the first rib it becomes the **axillary artery.** Its branches, which may be difficult to identify, supply the trunk and shoulder muscles. These are the **ventral thoracic artery** (to the pectoral muscles), the **long thoracic artery** (to pectoral muscles and latissimus dorsi), and the **subscapular artery** (to the trunk muscles). As the axillary artery enters the arm, it is called the **brachial artery,** and it travels with the median nerve down

the length of the humerus. At the elbow, the brachial artery branches to produce the two major arteries serving the forearm and hand, the **radial** and **ulnar arteries.**

4. Return to the thorax, lift the left lung, and follow the course of the *descending aorta* through the thoracic cavity. The esophagus overlies it along its course. Notice the paired **intercostal arteries** that branch laterally from the aorta in the thoracic region.

5. Follow the aorta through the diaphragm into the abdominal cavity. Carefully pull the peritoneum away from its ventral surface and identify the following vessels:

Celiac trunk: The first branch diverging from the aorta immediately as it enters the abdominal cavity; supplies the stomach, liver, gallbladder, pancreas, and spleen. (Trace as many of its branches to these organs as possible.)

Superior mesenteric artery: Immediately posterior to the celiac trunk; supplies the small intestine and most of the large intestine. (Spread the mesentery of the small intestine to observe the branches of this artery as they run to supply the small intestine.)

Adrenolumbar arteries: Paired arteries diverging from the aorta slightly posterior to the superior mesenteric artery; supply the muscles of the body wall and adrenal glands.

Renal arteries: Paired arteries supplying the kidneys.

Gonadal arteries (testicular or ovarian): Paired arteries supplying the gonads.

Inferior mesenteric artery: An unpaired thin vessel arising from the ventral surface of the aorta posterior to the gonadal arteries; supplies the second half of the large intestine.

Iliolumbar arteries: Paired, rather large arteries that supply the body musculature in the iliolumbar region.

External iliac arteries: Paired arteries which continue through the body wall and pass under the inguinal ligament to the hindlimb.

6. After giving off the external iliac arteries, the aorta persists briefly and then divides into three arteries: the two **internal iliac arteries,** which supply the pelvic viscera, and the **median sacral artery.** As the median sacral artery enters the tail, it comes to be called the **caudal artery.** (Note that there is no common iliac artery in the cat.)

7. Trace the external iliac artery into the thigh, where it becomes the **femoral artery.** The femoral artery is most easily identified in the *femoral triangle* at the medial surface of the upper thigh. Follow the femoral artery as it courses through the thigh (along with the femoral vein and nerve) and gives off branches to the thigh muscles. As you approach the knee, the **saphenous artery** branches off the femoral artery to supply the medial portion of the leg. The femoral artery then descends deep to the knee to become the **popliteal artery** in the popliteal region. The popliteal artery in turn gives off two main branches, the **sural artery** and the **posterior tibial artery,** and continues as the **anterior tibial artery.** These branches supply the leg and foot. ▬

Dissection of the Blood Vessels of the Cat

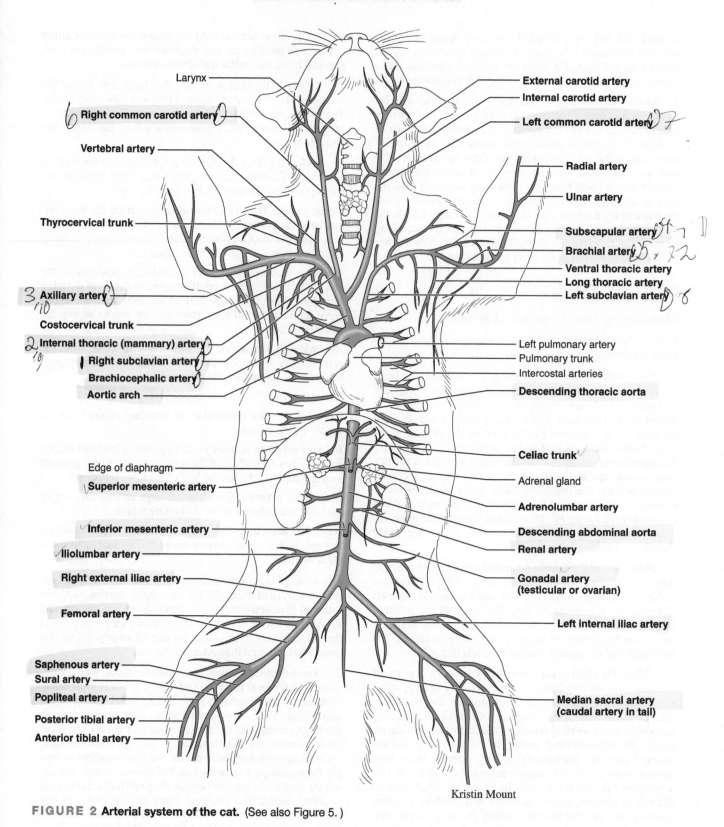

Larynx

External carotid artery
Internal carotid artery
Right common carotid artery
Left common carotid artery

Vertebral artery

Radial artery

Ulnar artery

Thyrocervical trunk

Subscapular artery
Brachial artery
Ventral thoracic artery
Long thoracic artery
Left subclavian artery

Axillary artery

Costocervical trunk

Internal thoracic (mammary) artery

Right subclavian artery

Brachiocephalic artery

Aortic arch

Left pulmonary artery
Pulmonary trunk
Intercostal arteries
Descending thoracic aorta

Edge of diaphragm

Celiac trunk

Adrenal gland

Superior mesenteric artery

Adrenolumbar artery

Inferior mesenteric artery

Descending abdominal aorta

Iliolumbar artery

Renal artery

Right external iliac artery

Gonadal artery
(testicular or ovarian)

Femoral artery

Left internal iliac artery

Saphenous artery
Sural artery
Popliteal artery
Posterior tibial artery
Anterior tibial artery

Median sacral artery
(caudal artery in tail)

Kristin Mount

FIGURE 2 Arterial system of the cat. (See also Figure 5.)

Identifying the Veins of the Cat

Refer to Figure 3 and to summary Figure 5 as you study the venous system of the cat. Keep in mind that the vessels are named for the region drained, not for the point of union with other veins.

1. Reidentify the **precava** as it enters the right atrium. Trace it anteriorly to identify veins that enter it.

Azygos vein: Passing directly into its dorsal surface; drains the thoracic intercostal muscles.

Internal thoracic (mammary) veins: Drain the chest and abdominal walls.

Right vertebral vein: Drains the spinal cord and brain; usually enters right side of precava approximately at the level of the internal thoracic veins but may enter the brachiocephalic vein in your specimen.

Right and left brachiocephalic veins: Form the precava by their union.

2. Reflect the pectoral muscles, and trace the brachiocephalic vein laterally. Identify the two large veins that unite to form it—the external jugular vein and the subclavian vein. Notice that this differs from humans, whose brachiocephalic veins are formed by the union of the internal jugular and subclavian veins.

3. Follow the **external jugular vein** as it courses anteriorly along the side of the neck to the point where it is joined on its medial surface by the **internal jugular vein.** The internal jugular veins are small and may be difficult to identify in the cat. Notice the difference in cat and human jugular veins. The internal jugular is considerably larger in humans and drains into the subclavian vein. In the cat, the external jugular is larger, and the internal jugular vein drains into it. Several other vessels drain into the external jugular vein (transverse scapular vein draining the shoulder, facial veins draining the head, and others). These are not discussed here but are shown on the figure and may be traced if time allows. Also, identify the *common carotid artery,* since it accompanies the internal jugular vein in this region, and attempt to find the *sympathetic trunk,* which is located in the same area running lateral to the trachea.

4. Return to the shoulder region and follow the course of the **subclavian vein** as it moves laterally toward the arm. It becomes the **axillary vein** as it passes in front of the first rib and runs through the brachial plexus, giving off several branches, the first of which is the **subscapular vein.** The subscapular vein drains the proximal part of the arm and shoulder. The four other branches that receive drainage from the shoulder, pectoral, and latissimus dorsi muscles are shown in the figure but need not be identified in this dissection.

5. Follow the axillary vein into the arm, where it becomes the **brachial vein.** You can locate this vein on the medial side of the arm accompanying the brachial artery and nerve. Trace it to the point where it receives the **radial** and **ulnar veins** (which drain the forelimb) at the inner bend of the elbow. Also locate the superficial **cephalic vein** on the dorsal side of the arm. It communicates with the brachial vein via the median cubital vein in the elbow region and then enters the transverse scapular vein in the shoulder.

6. Reidentify the **postcaval vein,** and trace it to its passage through the diaphragm. Notice again as you follow its course that the **intercostal veins** drain into a much smaller vein lying dorsal to the postcava, the **azygos vein.**

7. Attempt to identify the **hepatic veins** entering the postcava from the liver. These may be seen if some of the anterior liver tissue is scraped away where the postcava enters the liver.

8. Displace the intestines to the left side of the body cavity, and proceed posteriorly to identify the following veins in order. All of these veins empty into the postcava and drain the organs served by the same-named arteries. In the cat, variations in the connections of the veins to be located are common, and in some cases the postcaval vein may be double below the level of the renal veins. If you observe deviations, call them to the attention of your instructor.

Adrenolumbar veins: From the adrenal glands and body wall.

Renal veins: From the kidneys (it is common to find two renal veins on the right side).

Gonadal veins (testicular or ovarian veins): The left vein of this venous pair enters the left renal vein anteriorly.

Iliolumbar veins: Drain muscles of the back.

Common iliac veins: Unite to form the postcava.

The common iliac veins are formed in turn by the union of the **internal iliac** and **external iliac veins.** The more medial internal iliac veins receive branches from the pelvic organs and gluteal region, whereas the external iliac vein receives venous drainage from the lower extremity. As the external iliac vein enters the thigh by running beneath the inguinal ligament, it receives the **deep femoral vein,** which drains the thigh and the external genital region. Just inferior to that point, the external iliac vein becomes the **femoral vein,** which receives blood from the thigh, leg, and foot. Follow the femoral vein down the thigh to identify the **great saphenous vein,** a superficial vein that courses up the inner aspect of the calf and across the inferior portion of the gracilis muscle (accompanied by the great saphenous artery and nerve) to enter the femoral vein. The femoral vein is formed by the union of this vein and the popliteal vein. The **popliteal vein** is located deep in the thigh beneath the semimembranosus and semitendinosus muscles in the popliteal space accompanying the popliteal artery. Trace the popliteal vein to its point of division into the **posterior** and **anterior tibial veins,** which drain the leg.

Dissection of the Blood Vessels of the Cat

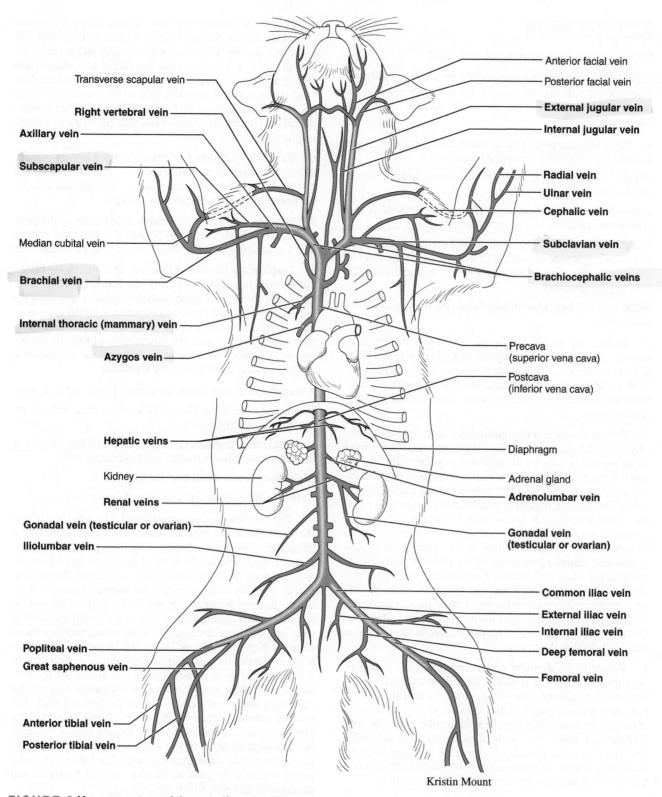

FIGURE 3 Venous system of the cat. (See also Figure 5.)

Kristin Mount

34

Dissection of the Blood Vessels of the Cat

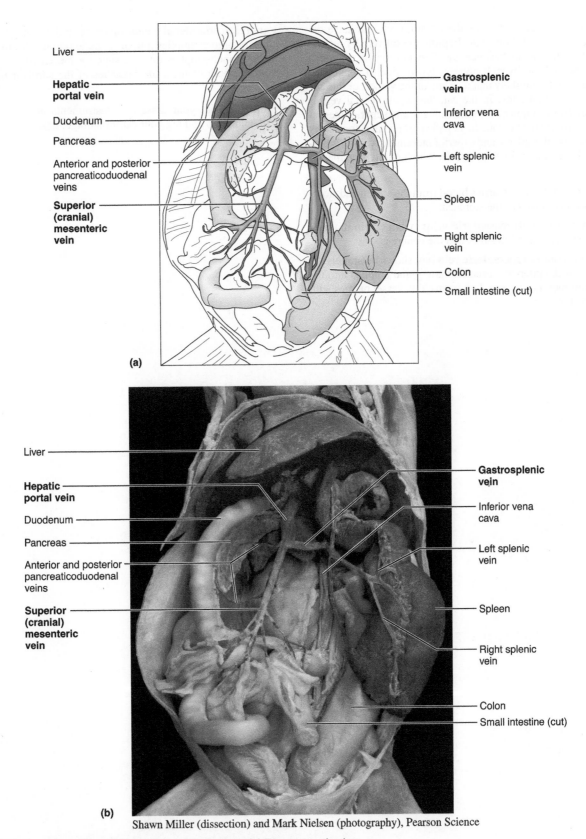

Liver

Hepatic portal vein

Duodenum

Pancreas

Anterior and posterior pancreaticoduodenal veins

Superior (cranial) mesenteric vein

Gastrosplenic vein

Inferior vena cava

Left splenic vein

Spleen

Right splenic vein

Colon

Small intestine (cut)

(a)

(b)

Shawn Miller (dissection) and Mark Nielsen (photography), Pearson Science

FIGURE 4 Hepatic portal circulation of the cat. (a) Diagrammatic view.
(b) Photograph of hepatic portal system of the cat just posterior to the liver and pancreas.
Intestines have been partially removed. The mesentery of the small intestine has been
partially dissected to show the veins of the portal system.

9. In your specimen, trace the hepatic portal drainage depicted in Figure 4. Locate the **hepatic portal vein** by removing the peritoneum between the first portion of the small intestine and the liver. It appears brown due to coagulated blood, and it is unlikely that it or any of the vessels of this circulation contain latex. In the cat, the hepatic portal vein is formed by the union of the gastrosplenic and superior mesenteric veins. (In the human, the hepatic portal vein is formed by the union of the splenic and superior mesenteric veins.) If possible, locate the following vessels, which empty into the hepatic portal vein.

Gastrosplenic vein: Carries blood from the spleen and stomach; located dorsal to the stomach.

Superior (cranial) mesenteric vein: A large vein draining the small and large intestines and the pancreas.

Inferior (caudal) mesenteric vein (not shown): Parallels the course of the inferior mesenteric artery and empties into the superior mesenteric vein. In humans, this vessel merges with the splenic vein.

Pancreaticoduodenal veins (anterior and posterior): The anterior branch empties into the hepatic portal vein; the posterior branch empties into the superior mesenteric vein. (In humans, both of these are branches of the superior mesenteric vein.)

Properly clean your dissecting instruments and dissecting pan, and wrap and tag your cat for storage. ■

Dissection of the Blood Vessels of the Cat

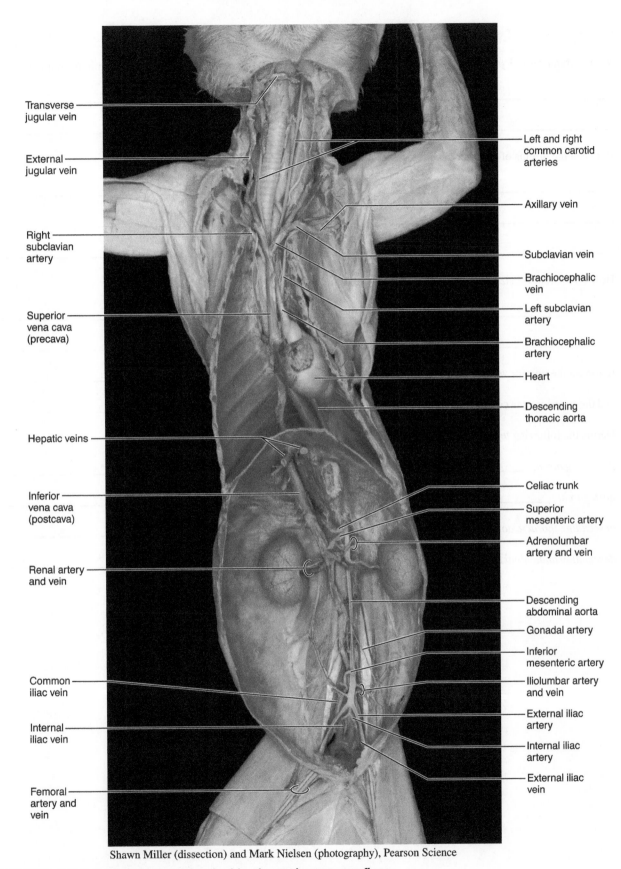

Transverse jugular vein

External jugular vein

Right subclavian artery

Superior vena cava (precava)

Hepatic veins

Inferior vena cava (postcava)

Renal artery and vein

Common iliac vein

Internal iliac vein

Femoral artery and vein

Left and right common carotid arteries

Axillary vein

Subclavian vein

Brachiocephalic vein

Left subclavian artery

Brachiocephalic artery

Heart

Descending thoracic aorta

Celiac trunk

Superior mesenteric artery

Adrenolumbar artery and vein

Descending abdominal aorta

Gonadal artery

Inferior mesenteric artery

Iliolumbar artery and vein

External iliac artery

Internal iliac artery

External iliac vein

Shawn Miller (dissection) and Mark Nielsen (photography), Pearson Science

FIGURE 5 Cat dissected to reveal major blood vessels: summary figure.

Dissection of the Blood Vessels of the Cat

DISSECTION REVIEW

1. What differences did you observe between the origins of the left common carotid arteries in the cat and in the human?

    _____

    _____

    Between the origins of the internal and external iliac arteries?

    _____

    _____

    _____

2. How do the relative sizes of the external and internal jugular veins differ in the human and the cat?

    _____

    _____

3. In the cat the inferior vena cava is called the _____

    and the superior vena cava is referred to as the _____

4. Define the following terms.

    ascending aorta: _____

    aortic arch: _____

    descending thoracic aorta: _____

    descending abdominal aorta: _____

The Main Lymphatic Ducts of the Cat

MATERIALS

- ☐ Disposable gloves
- ☐ Dissecting instruments and tray
- ☐ Animal specimen from previous dissections
- ☐ Embalming fluid
- ☐ Paper towels

OBJECTIVE

To compare and contrast lymphatic structures of the cat to those of a human.

ACTIVITY

Identifying the Main Lymphatic Ducts of the Cat

1. Don disposable gloves. Obtain your cat and a dissecting tray and instruments. Because lymphatic vessels are extremely thin-walled, it is difficult to locate them in a dissection unless the animal has been triply injected (with yellow or green latex for the lymphatic system). However, the large thoracic duct can be localized and identified.

2. Move the thoracic organs to the side to locate the **thoracic duct.** Typically it lies just to the left of the mid-dorsal line, abutting the dorsal aspect of the descending aorta. It is usually about the size of pencil lead and red-brown with a segmented or beaded appearance caused by the valves within it. Trace it anteriorly to the site where it passes behind the left brachiocephalic vein and then bends and enters the venous system at the junction of the left subclavian and external jugular veins. If the veins are well injected, some of the blue latex may have slipped past the valves and entered the first portion of the thoracic duct.

3. While in this region, also attempt to identify the short **right lymphatic duct** draining into the right subclavian vein, and notice the collection of lymph nodes in the axillary region.

4. If the cat is triply injected, trace the thoracic duct posteriorly to identify the **cisterna chyli,** the saclike enlargement of its distal end. This structure, which receives fat-rich lymph from the intestine, begins at the level of the diaphragm and can be localized posterior to the left kidney.

5. When you finish identifying these lymphatic structures, clean the dissecting instruments and tray, and properly wrap the cat and return it to storage. ▬

PAL

For access to anatomical models and more, check out Practice Anatomy Lab.

From Dissection Exercise 5 of *Human Anatomy & Physiology Laboratory Manual, PhysioEx 9.0 Update, Cat Version*, Tenth Edition.
Elaine N. Marieb, Susan J. Mitchell. Copyright © 2012 by Pearson Education, Inc. Published by Pearson Benjamin Cummings. All rights reserved.

1. How does the cat's lymphatic drainage pattern compare to that of humans? _____

_____

2. What is the role of the following? _____

    a.   thoracic duct _____

_____

    b.   right lymphatic duct _____

_____

Dissection of the Respiratory System of the Cat

MATERIALS

- ☐ Disposable gloves
- ☐ Dissecting instruments and tray
- ☐ Animal specimen from previous dissections
- ☐ Embalming fluid
- ☐ Paper towels
- ☐ Stereomicroscope

OBJECTIVE

To identify the major respiratory system organs in a dissected animal.

In this dissection exercise, you will be examining both the gross and fine structure of respiratory system organs. Don disposable gloves and then obtain your dissection animal, and dissecting tray and instruments.

ACTIVITY 1

Identifying Organs of the Respiratory System

1.   Examine the external nares, oral cavity, and oral pharynx. Use a probe to demonstrate the continuity between the oral pharynx and the nasal pharynx above.

2.   After securing the animal to the dissecting tray dorsal surface down, expose the more distal respiratory structures by retracting the cut muscle and rib cage. Do not sever nerves and blood vessels located on either side of the trachea if these have not been studied. If you have not previously opened the thoracic cavity, make a medial longitudinal incision through the neck muscles and thoracic musculature to expose and view the thoracic organs.

3.   Using the orientation Figure 1 and the photos in Figures 2 and 3 as guides, identify the structures named in items 3 through 5. Examine the **trachea,** and determine by finger examination whether the cartilage rings are complete or incomplete posteriorly. Locate the **thyroid gland** inferior to the larynx on the trachea. Free the **larynx** from the attached muscle tissue for ease of examination. Identify the **thyroid** and **cricoid cartilages** and the flaplike **epiglottis.** Find the **hyoid bone,** located anterior to the larynx. Make a longitudinal incision through the ventral wall of the larynx and locate the *true* and *false vocal cords* on the inner wall (see Figure 2).

4.   Locate the large *right* and *left common carotid arteries* and the *internal jugular veins* on either side of the trachea. Also locate a conspicuous white band, the *vagus nerve,* which lies alongside the trachea, adjacent to the common carotid artery.

PAL

For access to anatomical models and more, check out Practice Anatomy Lab.

From Dissection Exercise 6 of *Human Anatomy & Physiology Laboratory Manual, PhysioEx 9.0 Update, Cat Version*, Tenth Edition.
Elaine N. Marieb, Susan J. Mitchell. Copyright © 2012 by Pearson Education, Inc. Published by Pearson Benjamin Cummings. All rights reserved.

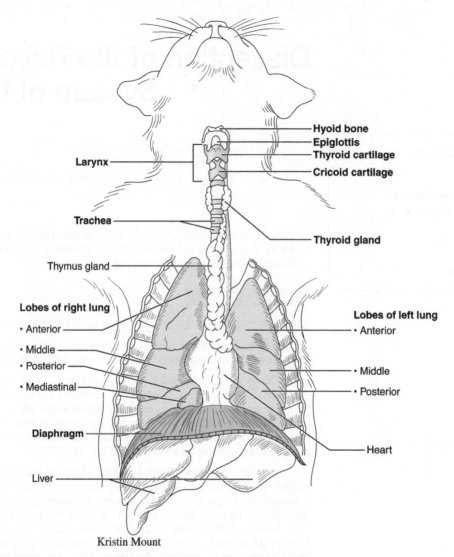

Hyoid bone
Epiglottis
Thyroid cartilage
Cricoid cartilage

Larynx

Trachea

Thyroid gland

Thymus gland

Lobes of right lung

• Anterior

• Middle

• Posterior

• Mediastinal

Lobes of left lung

• Anterior

• Middle

• Posterior

Diaphragm

Heart

Liver

Kristin Mount

FIGURE 1 Respiratory system of the cat. (See also the photo in Figure 3.)

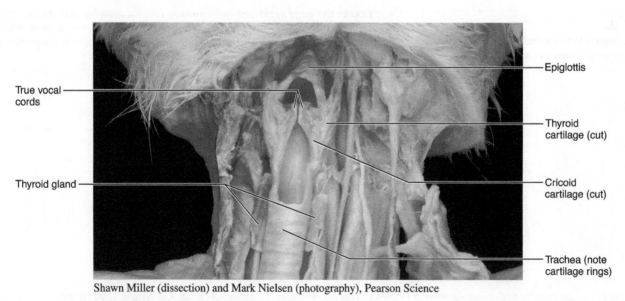

True vocal cords

Epiglottis

Thyroid cartilage (cut)

Thyroid gland

Cricoid cartilage (cut)

Trachea (note cartilage rings)

Shawn Miller (dissection) and Mark Nielsen (photography), Pearson Science

FIGURE 2 Larynx (opened), trachea, and thyroid gland.

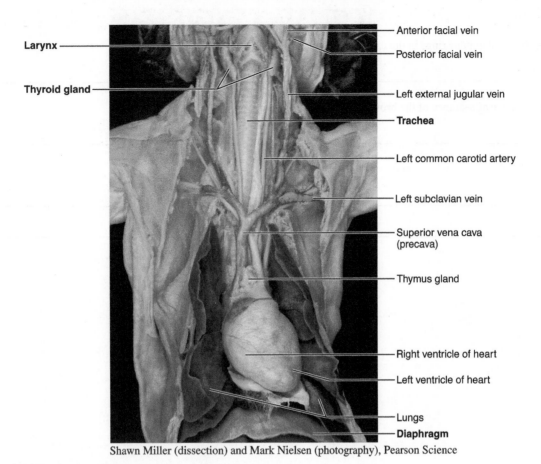

Larynx

Thyroid gland

Anterior facial vein

Posterior facial vein

Left external jugular vein

Trachea

Left common carotid artery

Left subclavian vein

Superior vena cava (precava)

Thymus gland

Right ventricle of heart

Left ventricle of heart

Lungs

Diaphragm

Shawn Miller (dissection) and Mark Nielsen (photography), Pearson Science

FIGURE 3 Photograph of the respiratory system of the cat.

5.   Examine the contents of the thoracic cavity (see Figure 3). Follow the trachea as it bifurcates into two *primary bronchi,* which plunge into the **lungs.** Note that there are two *pleural cavities* containing the lungs and that each lung is composed of many lobes. In humans there are three lobes in the right lung and two in the left. How does this compare to what is seen in the cat?

_____

_____

In the mediastinum, identify the *pericardial sac* (if it is still present) containing the heart. Examine the *pleura,* and note its exceptionally smooth texture.

6.   Locate the **diaphragm** and the **phrenic nerve.** The phrenic nerve, clearly visible as a white "thread" running along the pericardium to the diaphragm, controls the activity of the diaphragm in breathing. Lift one lung and find the esophagus beneath the parietal pleura. Follow it through the diaphragm to the stomach. ▮

ACTIVITY 2

Observing Lung Tissue Microscopically

Make a longitudinal incision in the outer tissue of one lung lobe beginning at a primary bronchus. Attempt to follow part of the respiratory tree from this point down into the smaller subdivisions. Carefully observe the cut lung tissue (under a stereoscope, if one is available), noting the richness of the vascular supply and the irregular or spongy texture of the lung. ▮

1. Are the cartilaginous rings in the cat trachea complete or incomplete?

   _____

2. Describe the appearance of the bronchial tree in the cat lung.

   _____

3. Describe the appearance of lung tissue under the dissection microscope.

   _____

   _____

Dissection of the Digestive System of the Cat

MATERIALS

- ☐ Disposable gloves
- ☐ Dissecting instruments and tray
- ☐ Animal specimen from previous dissections
- ☐ Bone cutters
- ☐ Hand lens
- ☐ Embalming fluid
- ☐ Paper towels

OBJECTIVES

1. To identify on a dissected animal the organs composing the alimentary canal, and to name their subdivisions if any.
2. To name and identify the accessory organs of digestion in the dissection animal, and to indicate their function.

Don gloves and obtain your dissection animal. Secure it to the dissecting tray, dorsal surface down. Obtain all necessary dissecting instruments. If you have completed the dissection of the circulatory and respiratory systems, the abdominal cavity is already exposed and many of the digestive system structures have been previously identified. However, duplication of effort generally provides a good learning experience, so all of the digestive system structures will be traced and identified in this exercise.

If the abdominal cavity has not been previously opened, make a midline incision from the rib cage to the pubic symphysis as shown in Figure 1. Then make four

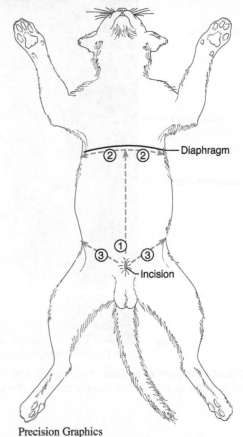

Precision Graphics

FIGURE 1 Incisions to be made in opening the ventral body cavity of the cat. Numbers indicate sequence.

PAL

For access to anatomical models and more, check out Practice Anatomy Lab.

From Dissection Exercise 7 of *Human Anatomy & Physiology Laboratory Manual, PhysioEx 9.0 Update, Cat Version*, Tenth Edition.
Elaine N. Marieb, Susan J. Mitchell. Copyright © 2012 by Pearson Education, Inc. Published by Pearson Benjamin Cummings. All rights reserved.

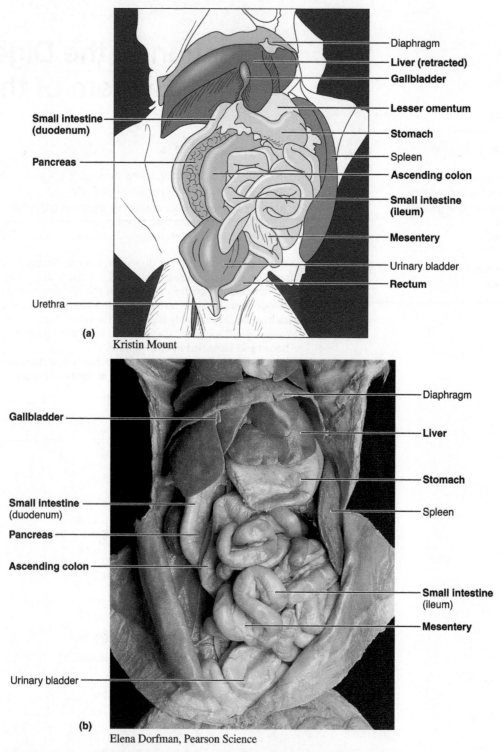

Kristin Mount

Elena Dorfman, Pearson Science

FIGURE 2 **Digestive organs of the cat.** **(a)** Diagrammatic view. **(b)** Photograph. The greater omentum has been cut from its attachment to the stomach.

lateral cuts—two parallel to the rib cage and two at the inferior margin of the abdominal cavity so that the abdominal wall can be reflected back while you examine the abdominal contents. Observe the shiny membrane lining the inner surface of the abdominal wall, which is the **parietal peritoneum.**

ACTIVITY 1

Identifying Alimentary Canal Organs

1. Using Figure 2, locate the abdominal alimentary canal structures.

2. Identify the large reddish brown **liver** (Figure 3) just beneath the diaphragm and the greater omentum, an apron of mesentery riddled with fat (not shown), that covers the abdominal contents. The greater omentum is attached to the greater curvature of the stomach; it assists in regulating body temperature, and its phagocytic cells help to protect the body. Lift the greater omentum, noting its two-layered structure and attachments, and lay it to the side or remove it to make subsequent organ identifications easier. Does the liver of the cat have the same number of lobes as the human liver?

3. Lift the liver and examine its inferior surface to locate the **gallbladder,** a dark greenish sac embedded in the liver's ventral surface. Identify the **falciform ligament,** a delicate layer of mesentery separating the main lobes of the liver

(right and left median lobes) and attaching the liver superiorly to the abdominal wall. Also identify the thickened area along the posterior edge of the falciform ligament, the *round ligament,* or *ligamentum teres,* a remnant of the umbilical vein of the embryo.

4. Displace the left lobes of the liver to expose the **stomach.** Identify the esophagus as it enters the stomach and the cardiac, fundic, body, and pyloric regions of the stomach. What is the general shape of the stomach?

Locate the **lesser omentum,** the serous membrane attaching the lesser curvature of the stomach to the liver, and identify the large tongue-like spleen curving around the greater curvature of the stomach.

Make an incision through the stomach wall to expose the inner surface of the stomach. When the stomach is empty, its mucosa is thrown into large folds called **rugae.** Can you see rugae? As the stomach fills, the rugae gradually disappear and are no longer visible. Identify the **pyloric sphincter** at the distal end of the stomach.

5. Lift the stomach and locate the **pancreas,** which appears as a grayish or brownish diffuse glandular mass in the mesentery. It extends from the vicinity of the spleen and greater curvature of the stomach and wraps around the duodenum. Using Figure 3, attempt to find the **pancreatic duct** as it empties into the duodenum at a swollen area referred to as the **hepatopancreatic**

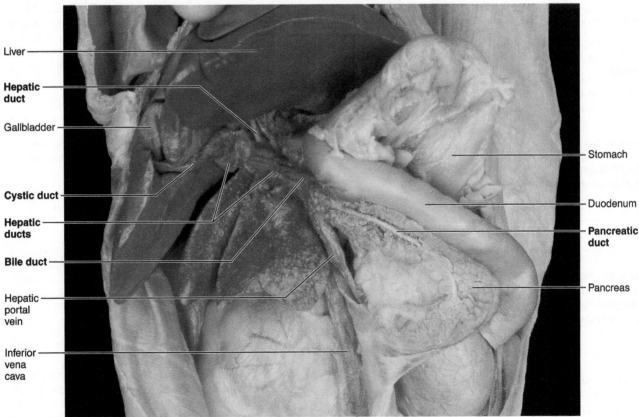

Shawn Miller (dissection) and Mark Nielsen (photography), Pearson Science

FIGURE 3 Ducts of the liver and pancreas.

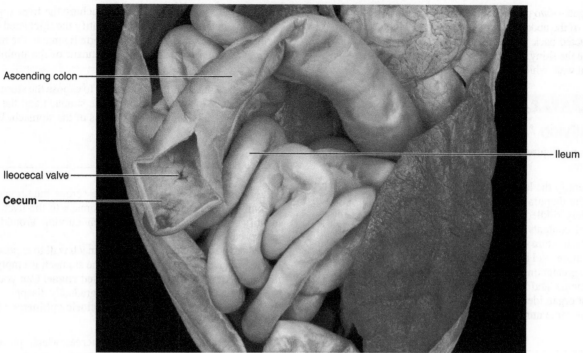

Ascending colon

Ileocecal valve

Cecum

Ileum

Shawn Miller (dissection) and Mark Nielsen (photography), Pearson Science

FIGURE 4 Ileocecal valve.

ampulla. Tease away the fine connective tissue, locate the **bile duct** close to the pancreatic duct, and trace its course superiorly to the point where it diverges into the **cystic duct** (gallbladder duct) and the **common hepatic duct** (duct from the liver). Notice that the duodenum assumes a looped position.

6. Lift the **small intestine** to investigate the manner in which it is attached to the posterior body wall by the **mesentery.**

Observe the mesentery closely. What types of structures do you see in this double peritoneal fold?

_____

Other than providing support for the intestine, what functions does the mesentery have?

_____

_____

Trace the course of the small intestine from its proximal (duodenal) end to its distal (ileal) end. Can you see any obvious differences in the external anatomy of the small intestine from one end to the other?

_____

With a scalpel, slice open the distal portion of the ileum and flush out the inner surface with water. Feel the inner surface with your fingertip. How does it feel?

Use a hand lens to see if you can see any **villi** and to locate the areas of lymphatic tissue called **Peyer's patches,** which appear as scattered white patches on the inner intestinal surface.

Return to the duodenal end of the small intestine. Make an incision into the duodenum. As before, flush the surface with water, and feel the inner surface. Does it feel any different from the ileal mucosa?

_____ If so, describe the difference. _____

_____

Use the hand lens to observe the villi. What differences do you see in the villi in the two areas of the small intestine?

_____

_____

7. Make an incision into the junction between the ileum and cecum to locate the ileocecal valve (Figure 4). Observe the **cecum,** the initial expanded part of the large intestine. (Lymph nodes may have to be removed from this area to observe it clearly.) Does the cat have an appendix?

_____

8. Identify the short ascending, transverse, and descending portions of the **colon** and the **mesocolon,** a membrane that attaches the colon to the posterior body wall. Trace the descending colon to the **rectum,** which penetrates the body wall, and identify the **anus** on the exterior surface of the specimen.

Identify the two portions of the peritoneum, the parietal peritoneum lining the abdominal wall (identified previously) and the visceral peritoneum, which is the outermost layer of the wall of the abdominal organs (serosa). ▆

ACTIVITY 2

Exposing and Viewing the Salivary Glands and Oral Cavity Structures

1. To expose and identify the **salivary glands,** which secrete saliva into the mouth, remove the skin from one side of the head and clear the connective tissue away from the angle of the jaw, below the ear, and superior to the masseter muscle. Many dark, kidney-shaped lymph nodes are in this area, and you should remove them if they obscure the salivary glands, which are light tan and lobular in texture. The cat possesses five pairs of salivary glands, but only those glands described in humans are easily localized and identified (Figure 5). Locate the **parotid gland** on the cheek just inferior to the ear. Follow its duct over the surface of the masseter muscle to the angle of the mouth. The **submandibular gland** is posterior to

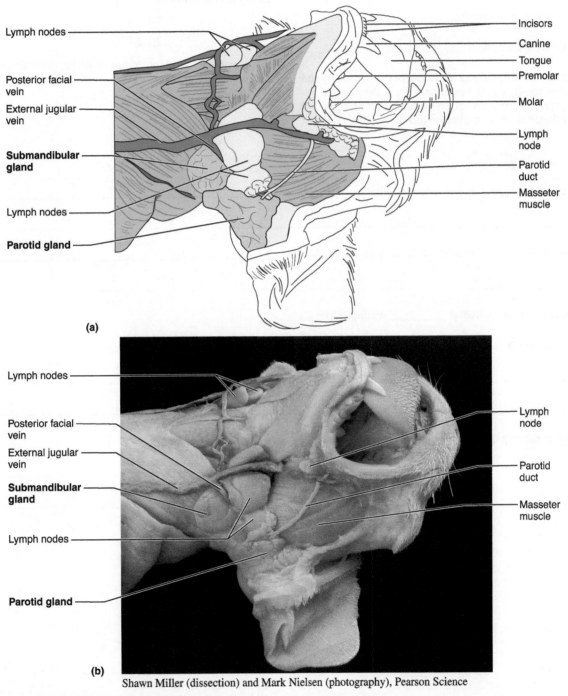

Shawn Miller (dissection) and Mark Nielsen (photography), Pearson Science

FIGURE 5 Salivary glands of the cat. (a) Diagrammatic view. **(b)** Photograph.

the parotid, near the angle of the jaw, and the **sublingual gland** is just anterior to the submandibular gland within the lower jaw. The ducts of the submandibular and sublingual glands run deep and parallel to each other and empty on the side of the frenulum of the tongue. These need not be identified on the cat.

2.   To expose and identify the structures of the oral cavity, cut through the mandibular angle with bone cutters to free the lower jaw from the maxilla.

Identify the **hard** and **soft palates,** and use a probe to trace the bony hard palate to its posterior limits. Note the transverse ridges, or *rugae,* on the hard palate, which play a role in holding food in place while chewing.

Do these appear in humans? _____

Does the cat have a uvula? _____

Identify the **oropharynx** at the rear of the oral cavity and the palatine tonsils on the posterior walls at the junction between the oral cavity and oropharynx. Identify the **tongue** and rub your finger across its surface to feel the papillae. Some of

the papillae, especially at the anterior end of the tongue, should feel sharp and bristly. These are the filiform papillae, which are much more numerous in the cat than in humans. What do you think their function is?

_____

Locate the **lingual frenulum** attaching the tongue to the floor of the mouth. Trace the tongue posteriorly until you locate the **epiglottis,** the flap of tissue that covers the entrance to the respiratory passageway when swallowing occurs. Identify the **esophageal opening** posterior to the epiglottis.

Observe the **teeth** of the cat. The dental formula for the adult cat is as follows:

$$\frac{3,1,3,1}{3,1,2,1} \times 2 = 30$$

3.   Prepare your cat for storage, wash the dissecting tray and instruments, and discard your gloves before continuing or leaving the laboratory. ▪

DISSECTION REVIEW

1.   Compare the appearance of tongue papillae in cats and humans. _____

_____

2.   Compare the number of lobes of the liver in cats and humans. _____

_____

3.   Does the cat have a uvula? _____ An appendix? _____

4.   Give an explanation for the different adult dental formulas in cats and humans.

_____

_____

5.   How do the villi differ in the duodenum and the ileum? Explain.

_____

_____

Dissection of the Urinary System of the Cat

MATERIALS

☐ Disposable gloves
☐ Dissecting instruments and tray
☐ Animal specimen from previous dissections
☐ Hand magnifying lens
☐ Embalming fluid
☐ Paper towel

OBJECTIVE

To identify on a dissection specimen the urinary system organs, and to describe the general function of each.

The structures of the reproductive and urinary systems are often considered together as the *urogenital system,* since they have common embryological origins. However, the emphasis in this dissection is on identifying the structures of the urinary tract (Figures 1 and 2) with only a few references to contiguous reproductive structures.

ACTIVITY

Identifying Organs of the Urinary System

1. Don gloves. Obtain your dissection specimen, and place it ventral side up on the dissecting tray. Reflect the abdominal viscera (most importantly the small intestine) to locate the kidneys high on the dorsal body wall (Figure 1). Note that the **kidneys** in the cat, as well as in the human, are retroperitoneal (behind the peritoneum). Carefully remove the peritoneum, and clear away the bed of fat that invests the kidneys. Then locate the adrenal (suprarenal) glands that lie superiorly and medial to the kidneys.

2. Identify the **renal artery** (red latex injected), the **renal vein** (blue latex injected), and the ureter at the hilum region of the kidney. (You may find two renal veins leaving one kidney in the cat but not in humans.)

3. To observe the gross internal anatomy of the kidney, slit the connective tissue *fibrous capsule* encasing a kidney and peel it back. Make a midfrontal cut through the kidney and examine one cut surface with a hand lens to identify the granular *cortex* and the central darker *medulla,* which will appear striated. Notice that the cat's renal medulla consists of just one pyramid as compared to the multipyramidal human kidney.

4. Trace the tubelike **ureters** to the **urinary bladder,** a smooth muscular sac located superiorly to the small intestine. If your cat is a female, be careful not to confuse the ureters with the uterine tubes, which lie superior to the bladder in the same general region (see Figure 1). Observe the sites where the ureters enter the bladder. How would you describe the entrance point anatomically?

_____

_____

PAL

For access to anatomical models and more, check out Practice Anatomy Lab.

5. Cut through the bladder wall, and examine the region of the urethral exit to see if you can discern any evidence of the *internal sphincter.*

From Dissection Exercise 8 of *Human Anatomy & Physiology Laboratory Manual, PhysioEx 9.0 Update, Cat Version*, Tenth Edition.
Elaine N. Marieb, Susan J. Mitchell. Copyright © 2012 by Pearson Education, Inc. Published by Pearson Benjamin Cummings. All rights reserved.

Dissection of the Urinary System of the Cat

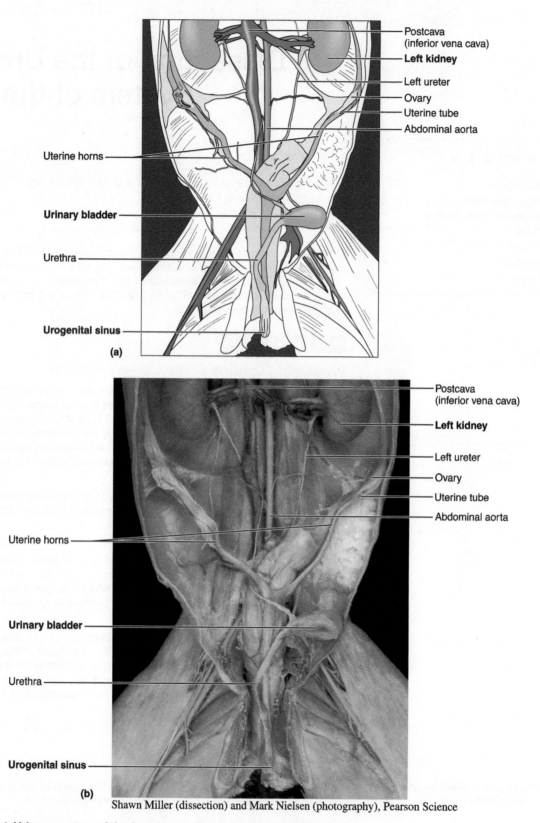

(a)

Postcava
(inferior vena cava)

Left kidney

Left ureter

Ovary

Uterine tube

Abdominal aorta

Uterine horns

Urinary bladder

Urethra

Urogenital sinus

Postcava
(inferior vena cava)

Left kidney

Left ureter

Ovary

Uterine tube

Abdominal aorta

Uterine horns

Urinary bladder

Urethra

Urogenital sinus

(b)

Shawn Miller (dissection) and Mark Nielsen (photography), Pearson Science

FIGURE 1 Urinary system of the female cat. (Reproductive structures are also indicated.) **(a)** Diagrammatic view. **(b)** Photograph of female urogenital system.

Dissection of the Urinary System of the Cat

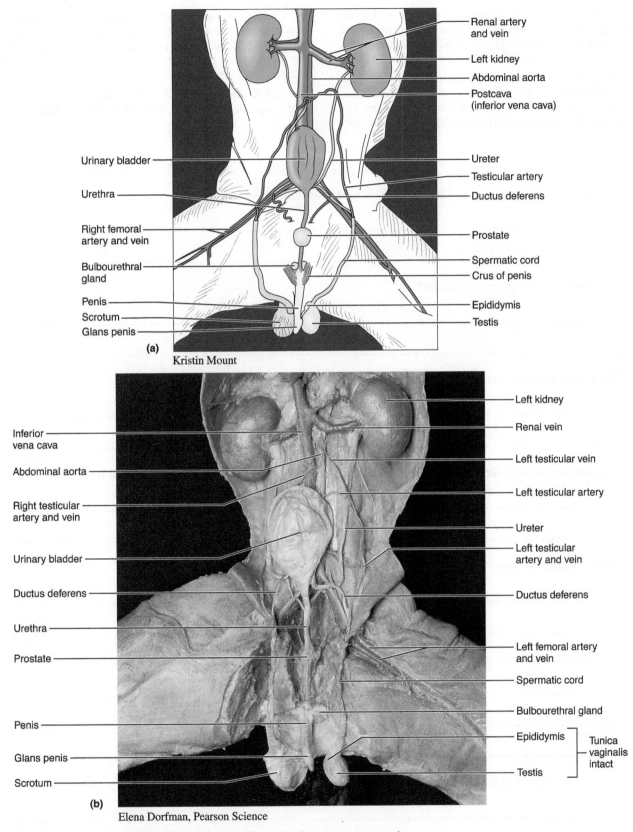

Renal artery and vein
Left kidney
Abdominal aorta
Postcava (inferior vena cava)
Urinary bladder
Urethra
Ureter
Testicular artery
Ductus deferens
Right femoral artery and vein
Bulbourethral gland
Prostate
Spermatic cord
Crus of penis
Penis
Scrotum
Glans penis
Epididymis
Testis

(a)

Kristin Mount

Left kidney
Renal vein
Inferior vena cava
Abdominal aorta
Left testicular vein
Left testicular artery
Right testicular artery and vein
Ureter
Left testicular artery and vein
Urinary bladder
Ductus deferens
Ductus deferens
Urethra
Prostate
Left femoral artery and vein
Spermatic cord
Bulbourethral gland
Penis
Epididymis
Tunica vaginalis intact
Glans penis
Testis
Scrotum

(b)

Elena Dorfman, Pearson Science

FIGURE 2 **Urinary system of the male cat.** (Reproductive structures are also indicated.) **(a)** Diagrammatic view. **(b)** Photograph of male urogenital system.

6. If your cat is a male, identify the prostate (part of the male reproductive system), which encircles the urethra distal to the neck of the bladder (Figure 2). Notice that the urinary bladder is somewhat fixed in position by ligaments.

7. Using a probe, trace the urethra as it exits from the bladder. In the male, it enters the penis. In the female cat, it terminates in the **urogenital sinus,** a common chamber into which both the vagina and the urethra empty. In the human female, the vagina and the urethra have separate external openings. Dissection to expose the urethra along its entire length should not be done at this time because of possible damage to the reproductive structures, which you may study in this course.

8. Before cleaning up the dissection materials, observe a cat of the opposite sex. Prepare your cat for storage. ▬

DISSECTION REVIEW

1. a. How does the position of the kidneys in the cat differ from their position in humans?

_____

_____

b. In what way is the position similar?

_____

_____

2. Distinguish between a ureter and the urethra.

_____

_____

3. How does the site of urethral emptying in the female cat differ from its termination point in the human female?

_____

_____

4. What is a urogenital sinus?

_____

_____

5. What gland encircles the neck of the bladder in the male? _____ Is this part of the urinary system?

_____ What is its function? _____

_____

_____

6. Compare the location of the adrenal glands in the cat to the location in humans.

_____

_____

Dissection of the Reproductive System of the Cat

OBJECTIVES

1. To identify the major reproductive structures of a male and a female dissection animal.
2. To recognize and discuss pertinent differences between the reproductive structures of humans and the dissection animal.

Don gloves, and obtain your cat, a dissecting tray, and the necessary dissecting instruments. After you have completed the study of the reproductive structures of your specimen, observe a cat of the opposite sex. (The following instructions assume that the abdominal cavity has been opened in previous dissection exercises.)

ACTIVITY 1

Identifying Organs of the Male Reproductive System

Refer to Figure 1 as you identify the male structures.

1. Identify the **penis,** and notice the prepuce covering the glans. Carefully cut through the skin overlying the penis to expose the cavernous tissue beneath, then cross section the penis to see the relative positioning of the three cavernous bodies.

2. Identify the **scrotum,** and then carefully make a shallow incision through the scrotum to expose the **testes.** Notice the abundant connective tissue stretching between the inner wall of the scrotum and testis surface, and note that the scrotum is divided internally.

3. Lateral to the medial aspect of the scrotal sac, locate the **spermatic cord,** which contains the testicular (spermatic) artery, vein, and nerve, as well as the ductus deferens, and follow it up through the inguinal canal into the abdominal cavity. (It is not necessary to cut through the pelvic bone; a slight tug on the spermatic cord in the scrotal sac region will reveal its position in the abdominal cavity.) Carefully loosen the spermatic cord from the connective tissue investing it, and follow its course as it travels superiorly in the pelvic cavity. Then follow the **ductus deferens** as it loops over the ureter, and then courses posterior to the bladder and enters the prostate. Using bone cutters, carefully make an incision through the pubic symphysis to follow the urethra.

4. Notice that the **prostate,** an enlarged whitish glandular mass abutting the urethra, is comparatively smaller in the cat than in the human, and it is more distal to the bladder. In the human, the prostate is immediately adjacent to the base of the bladder. Carefully slit open the prostate to follow the ductus deferens to the urethra, which exits from the bladder midline. The male cat urethra, like that of the human, serves as both a urinary and sperm duct. In the human, the ductus deferens is joined by the duct of the seminal vesicle to form the ejaculatory duct, which enters the prostate. Seminal vesicles are not present in the cat.

5. Trace the **urethra** to the proximal ends of the cavernous tissues of the penis, each of which is anchored to the ischium by a band of connective tissue called

PAL

For access to anatomical models and more, check out Practice Anatomy Lab.

Dissection of the Reproductive System of the Cat

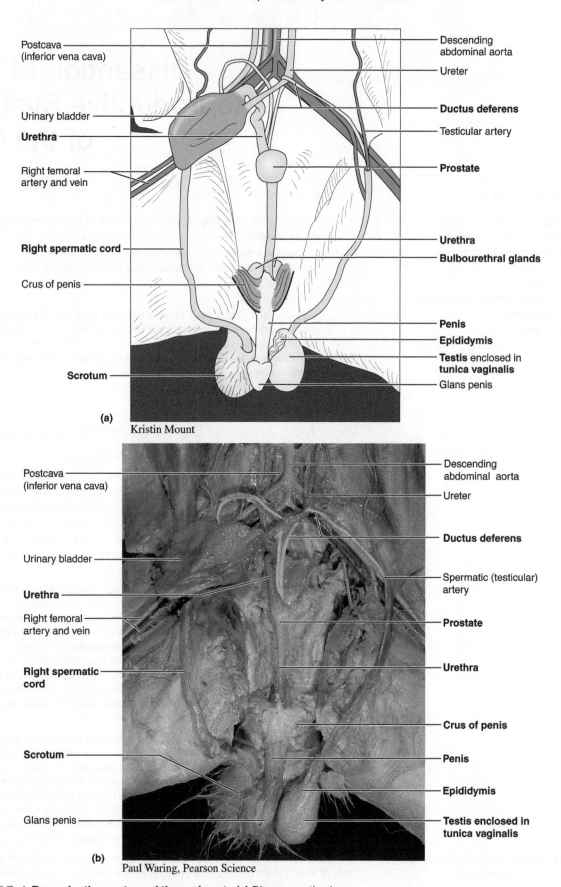

Postcava (inferior vena cava)

Urinary bladder

Urethra

Right femoral artery and vein

Right spermatic cord

Crus of penis

Scrotum

(a)
Kristin Mount

Descending abdominal aorta

Ureter

Ductus deferens

Testicular artery

Prostate

Urethra

Bulbourethral glands

Penis

Epididymis

Testis enclosed in **tunica vaginalis**

Glans penis

Postcava (inferior vena cava)

Urinary bladder

Urethra

Right femoral artery and vein

Right spermatic cord

Scrotum

Glans penis

(b)
Paul Waring, Pearson Science

Descending abdominal aorta

Ureter

Ductus deferens

Spermatic (testicular) artery

Prostate

Urethra

Crus of penis

Penis

Epididymis

Testis enclosed in tunica vaginalis

FIGURE 1 Reproductive system of the male cat. **(a)** Diagrammatic view.
(b) Photograph.

the **crus** of the penis. The crus is covered ventrally by the ischiocavernosus muscle and the **bulbourethral gland** lies beneath it (see Figure 1).

6.   Once again, turn your attention to the testis. Cut it from its attachment to the spermatic cord and carefully slit open the **tunica vaginalis** capsule enclosing it. Identify the **epididymis** running along one side of the testis. Make a longitudinal cut through the testis and epididymis. Can you see the tubular nature of the epididymis and the rete testis portion of the testis with the naked eye? ▆

Identifying Organs of the Female Reproductive System

Refer to Figure 2 showing a dissection of the urogenital system of the female cat as you identify the structures described below.

1.   Unlike the pear-shaped simplex, or one-part, uterus of the human, the uterus of the cat is Y-shaped (bipartite, or bicornuate) and consists of a **uterine body** from which two **uterine horns** (cornua) diverge. Such an enlarged uterus enables the animal to produce litters. Examine the abdominal cavity, and identify the bladder and the body of the uterus lying just dorsal to it.

2.   Follow one of the uterine horns as it travels superiorly in the body cavity. Identify the thin mesentery (the *broad ligament*) that helps anchor it and the other reproductive structures to the body wall. Approximately halfway up the length of the uterine horn, it should be possible to identify the more

important *round ligament,* a cord of connective tissue extending laterally and posteriorly from the uterine horn to the region of the body wall that would correspond to the inguinal region of the male.

3.   Examine the **uterine tube** and **ovary** at the distal end of the uterine horn just caudal to the kidney. Observe how the funnel-shaped end of the uterine tube curves around the ovary. As in the human, the distal end of the tube is fimbriated, or fringed, and the tube is lined with ciliated epithelium. The uterine tubes of the cat are tiny and much shorter than in the human. Identify the **ovarian ligament,** a short, thick cord that extends from the uterus to the ovary and anchors the ovary to the body wall. Also observe the *ovarian artery* and *vein* passing through the mesentery to the ovary and uterine structures.

4.   Return to the body of the uterus and follow it caudad to the bony pelvis. Use bone cutters to cut through the median line of the pelvis (the pubic symphysis), cutting carefully so you do not damage the urethra deep to it. Expose the pelvic region by pressing the thighs dorsally. Follow the uterine body caudally to where it narrows to its sphincterlike cervix, which protrudes into the vagina. Note the point where the urethra draining the bladder and the **vagina** enter a common chamber, the **urogenital sinus.** How does this anatomical arrangement compare to that seen in the human female?

_____

_____

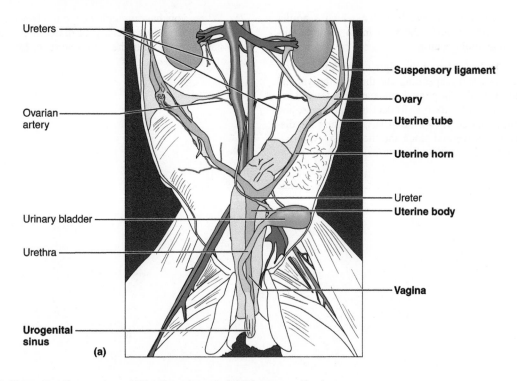

FIGURE 2 Reproductive system of the female cat. (a) Diagrammatic view.

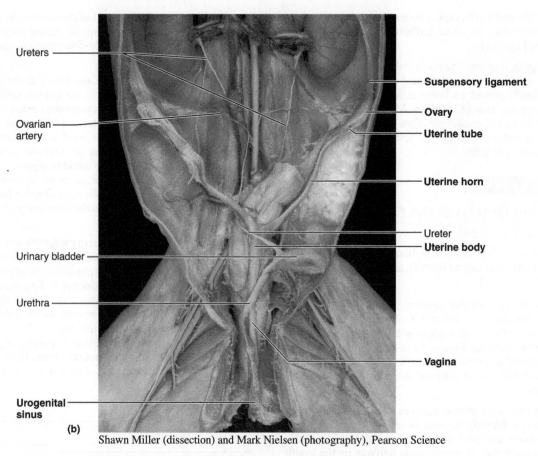

Ureters

Ovarian artery

Urinary bladder

Urethra

Urogenital sinus

(b)

Suspensory ligament

Ovary

Uterine tube

Uterine horn

Ureter

Uterine body

Vagina

Shawn Miller (dissection) and Mark Nielsen (photography), Pearson Science

FIGURE 2 *(continued)* **Reproductive system of the female cat. (b)** Photograph.

5. On the cat's exterior, observe the **vulva,** which is similar to the human vulva. Identify the slim **labia majora** surrounding the urogenital opening.

6. To determine the length of the vagina, which is difficult to ascertain by external inspection, slit through the vaginal wall just superior to the urogenital sinus and cut toward the body of the uterus with scissors. Reflect the cut edges, and identify the muscular cervix of the uterus. Measure the distance between the urogenital sinus and the cervix. Approximately how long is the vagina of the cat?

_____

7. When you have completed your observations of both male and female cats, clean your dissecting instruments and tray and properly wrap the cat for storage. ▬

1. The female cat has a _____ uterus; that of the human female is _____.

   Explain the difference in structure of these two uterine types. _____

   _____

   _____

2. What reproductive advantage is conferred by the feline uterine type?

   _____

   _____

3. Cite differences noted between the cat and the human relative to the following structures:

   uterine tubes or oviducts _____

   _____

   site of entry of ductus deferens into the urethra _____

   _____

   _____

   location of the prostate _____

   _____

   _____

   seminal vesicles _____

   _____

   urethral and vaginal openings in the female _____

   _____

   _____